CW00819995

WHY CAN'T I JUST ENJOY THINGS?

PIERRE NOVELLIE

WHY CAN'T I JUST ENJOY THINGS?

A Comedian's Guide to Autism

BLINK

bringing you closer

First published in the UK by Blink Publishing
An imprint of The Zaffre Publishing Group
A Bonnier Books UK company
4th Floor, Victoria House,
Bloomsbury Square,
London, WC1B 4DA

Owned by Bonnier Books
Sveavägen 56, Stockholm, Sweden

Hardback – 9781785121012
Ebook – 9781785121036
Audio Digital Download – 9781785121043

Designed by Envy Design Ltd

Printed and bound in Great Britain by Clays Ltd, Elcograf S.p.A.

1 3 5 7 9 10 8 6 4 2

Blink Publishing is an imprint of Bonnier Books UK
www.bonnierbooks.co.uk

With thanks to my parents, who explained the world to me.

Contents

Note to the Reader

A brief note on terminology: I use Asperger's syndrome when quoting or describing people or conversations that used the term, otherwise I will use autism and autism spectrum and avoid, where possible, using ASD or autism spectrum disorder in order to avoid legitimising the idea of a 'disorder' as opposed to simply a different neurotype. For accuracy, I have still used ASD when quoting or discussing official medical literature or policy. I have used 'non-autistic' instead of 'neurotypical' on occasions where I believe I am describing something exclusive to autistic people and not more generally to both autistic people, people with ADHD etc., but these differentiations are always up for debate. There are many elements of autism that I couldn't fit into the book and infinite perspectives out there that I cannot lay claim to, so please forgive me for missing out anything that you feel I should have included.

The Best Heckle
I Ever Had

When you are a professional stand-up the most common question people ask is: 'What is the best heckle you have ever had?' The second most common question is whether you're a full-time stand-up or a contributing member of society who does open mics a few times a year. People want to know if they're talking to a bold hobbyist or a true weirdo – and fair enough.

It's bad business to puncture popular myths but I find confirming people's cheerful misapprehensions, even when the misapprehensions benefit me personally, to be total agony, so here we go.[1] The terrible truth is that 99 per cent of heckles are absolute dogshit. If the public was truly, consistently funny, there would be no demand for stand-up. Everyone

---

1 I had to learn to stop correcting people when they claimed my career was doing better than it was. These were people who I wanted to think I was doing well! I mean, what the fuck is wrong with me? Let them think the good thing! As long as it's not something provably false. I mean, you don't want to look like a liar. I'm stressed thinking about it.

would just sit around the dinner table being spectacularly witty like characters in an American sitcom.

Every now and then a comedian will tell an anecdote about a particularly witty audience member or someone out in public, often on a bus. Generally, these stories are outright fiction. The comedian has imagined something witty for a given situation and has contrived to put their own carefully honed words into a random mouth, thereby boosting the perceived funniness of the comment. A filthy insult from someone who spent days writing it is embarrassing, but it's delightful off the cuff from a kindly pensioner. Context is everything and sometimes comedians make up the context or spice up the disappointing, realistic dialogue that the public provided. Warning signs that the heckle story you are hearing is bullshit are: the use of any phrase such as 'a voice from the back', 'clear as a bell', 'quick as a flash', any reference to a precocious child or an eccentric pensioner, or the story taking place in Glasgow or Liverpool (two cities that are, rightly or wrongly, obsessed with their own reputations as citadels of wit).

My own experiences of heckles is that they are generally committed by the sort of men who make awkward, ill-judged remarks in WhatsApp groups, or the 'funniest bloke in the office'. Men heckle to prove something about themselves to their social group and to test the comedian – so even if they lose the battle of wits, it was only as part of demonstrating their authority as examiner. They don't generally want to destroy the gig, but they do want to spray their scent on the evening as a whole. Women do sometimes heckle but are generally doing so because they are sincerely, personally offended by the comedian and wish to destroy them, if not derail the whole show. (Ask any comedian if stag dos or hen dos are worse, you will see.) Both men and women will also 'heckle' when paralytically drunk, but these are more noises than words and so are useless for comedic purposes. Trying to be witty in response to a senseless howl is like quoting Oscar Wilde at a barking dog.

So, caveats aside, this is the story of the best heckle I have ever had.

The year was 2022. The gig was called 'Comedy Den'. It was a small hipster night in the basement of a Bristol craft beer bar, run by the comedian Burt Williamson. I was headlining both evening shows. At the later show I was onstage at something like eleven o'clock on a Friday, so everyone was quite boozed. Some fans of the podcast I do with Phil Wang were in and the small basement crowd of about forty people was friendly and even a little conversational. It's not safe for comedians to admit that sometimes we like a slightly conversational crowd because only the wrong people take that as encouragement. It's like when a single woman complains that men don't approach women these days – the sort of man who leaps on that suggestion like a hungry toad is not the man she meant. Anyway, the crowd was the good kind of drunk and the good kind of responsive.

The two things you need to know for the heckle to make sense: the MC had talked to an audience member who was studying the fall of the Roman Republic and introduced me as a history buff. I had then come onstage and established my nerd credentials by reciting some facts about the fall of the Roman Republic, saying, 'You see? I'm just as much of a nerd as you were promised.'

3

WHY CAN'T I JUST ENJOY THINGS?

Secondly, the material I was doing was new material written for my show, *Why Can't I Just Enjoy Things?* Regardless, all the material was focused on either my social failures or areas where I did not gel with most people. Immediately prior to the heckle, I had finished a routine about how I didn't see eye to eye on something with an ex and did my best to explain my apparently unusual point of view. Suddenly, a man seated to my left piped up:

'You just sound like me.'

Now, when someone heckles you, the first thing you need to do is repeat the heckle into the microphone, especially at larger gigs. There is a good chance the audience didn't hear the heckle and so anything you say in return, however witty, will not get a laugh since the audience has no idea what you're replying to. Sneakily, it also gives the comedian a few crucial seconds to think and to look at the heckler for important information (appearance, age, level of drunkenness, social grouping, level of anger and so on). It also puts the onus on the heckler to repeat themselves or say another thing that can be responded to. If it sounds like I am turning comedy into something vaguely scientific, systematised and slightly manufactured, then God help you if you ever read about magic shows.

'What was that? You're saying I just sound like you?' I shot back, wittily, quick as a flash, etc.

'Well, I have Asperger's and you sound like me.'

I don't think he shrugged physically, but this heckle was certainly delivered with an implied shrug. The man was not shouting, or emotional, but offered this information the way one might tell a colleague that there's an easier route to work.

'You have Asperger's and you think that I just sound like you?' I said – repetition, my old friend! I was certainly surprised and needed the time.

'Yeah,' he said, nodding calmly.

'As in, you think that I might have it, too?' I pulled a baffled face, drew some laughs from the tension.

'Yeah, maybe!'

'Why?' I was genuinely interested now, but was trying to hide that from the audience. It can make you look distracted, or overly affected by the heckle.

'Well, you knew all that stuff about the fall of the Roman Republic.'

'That can't be the only criteria for Asperger's. I'm sure that's not the only question on the form. "Do you like history?" – I mimed a doctor ticking a single box on a form – 'Well then, I've got some news!'

A decent enough laugh to switch back to addressing the rest of the crowd and bring everyone back into listening mode. 'I've been heckled many times in my career but never this medically specifically.'

Decent enough laugh. I moved back into pre-existing material and thus the gig was broadly back on track. I had felt the crowd grow wary during my interaction with the man. This was partly because there was no clear moral high ground: yes, the man was heckling me that I might have a medical condition but, in fairness, it was a condition that he himself had and based on my own description of my own mind. Also, I wasn't annoyed and the man wasn't either, so there was no combativeness, nothing at stake. It was just a sort of unsettling demi-conversation about a sensitive issue conducted in public by accident. The audience may also have been worried about how I would react: would I be hurt, confused, dismissive, rude, escalatory? I could have ruined the gig by denying his claim so fervently I made it clear I found the idea of being like *him* horrifying or awful. But a few good-natured jokes and some vague meta commentary had us safely out of the woods for the remaining ten minutes or so of the set. It passed without incident and afterwards the other acts and I light-heartedly discussed the heckle in the bar upstairs.

In all honesty, it was not the first time someone had suggested it. Two or three friends of mine over the decade or so since I left university had put it to me, with varying degrees of gentleness, that I may be on the spectrum in some measurable way. They tended to say these things shortly after they had come to me for some advice or vented on some life issue or other and I had, in my opinion logically, helpfully pointed out the shortest route between them and their preferred outcome. This, I have learned, is often a mistake. When most people casually ask for your advice they are silently begging you to guess which answer they secretly want and immediately suggest it as the only sane course of action. Upon receiving my unsuitable advice, these friends would balk and suggest that, while logical, my advice was not delivered nicely enough and perhaps I was on the spectrum (or simply, 'God, you're such a robot!').

You might be wondering: Why was this heckle such an important revelation given your apparent years of Spock-like blundering? The distinction is that these friends who found me robotic were often my most emotions-led, impulsive and touchy-feely friends; people for whom the phrase 'Trust your heart!' was actual advice, people who would struggle to break up with a serial killer, if the killer seemed like he was doing his best to stop. I felt within my rights to think, 'Well of course I'm robotic *compared to you.*' The difference that night at the gig was that this heckler, well, he was qualified! The man had the damn thing himself; he was recognising himself in me, something far more profound and meaningful.

The next morning, after an impersonal night in a chain hotel, I was on the train from Bristol back to London mulling over the heckle. It had left my confidence in my own 'normality' shaken but, if you'd asked me then and there, I'd still have wagered I fell on the 'neurotypical' end of things. I had been friendly[2] with a guy at school with Asperger's and I didn't feel kinship with him on that basis and, thinking back during that train journey, I still didn't. I confess I had even taken some of the shorter online spectrum questionnaires[3] in moments of idleness, though no more seriously than I had enjoyed taking online tests for anything from 'Where on the political spectrum am I?' to 'Flags of the world', and the autism tests had yielded vague and varying results. Despite this, I figured I would use the dead time of the train to try again and came across a website called Embrace Autism, a very

---

2 Friends? Friendly? Was friends with but see sometimes but not often? The categorisation of relationships has always filled me with panic since other people's expectations sometimes don't match my own and accidentally wounding a friend by misdescribing your relationship with them is horrifying.

3 Unlike online IQ tests, autistic spectrum disorder (ASD) questionnaires can be the same ones a medical professional would have you fill out. Results will still be more accurate with the guidance of a qualified professional but you can glean your place on the spectrum within an acceptable margin of error, in my opinion, if they are the longer and more modern tests.

useful website scattered with the sort of unsettlingly cheerful cartoons you'd expect to find in a children's hospital. The site hosts many, if not all, of the questionnaires one would use to measure neurodivergence, along with helpful annotations explaining terminology, which questions or concepts are now out of date and so on. You can easily fill them in online, even if you're drinking a pint of black coffee on a train sat next to a coughing lady. I filled in pretty much all the questionnaires and, when the autistic spectrum ones came back with a high score, I filled them in multiple times with different answers for the borderline questions to achieve an average, and to see the highest to lowest range of score I could achieve without lying. Honestly, at that point the website should have had a pop-up that said: 'Congratulations, only an autist would have this level of dedication to statistical accuracy, please consult your nearest model railway salesperson.'

I have to admit I was a little unsettled at this point. How was I scoring this high? I had met quite a few Asperger's/ autistic people in my life and I had never particularly felt that they were all kindred spirits. In fact I had found some of them deeply frustrating. Besides that, I was a professional comedian with friends and a romantic partner and all the stereotypes were clear that made me far too sociable to be on the spectrum. Nevertheless, however 'normally' I attempted to answer the questionnaires, I could not score within the normal range without giving false answers. Shit. Well, time to do an enormous amount of research that becomes an obsessive interest over the next few weeks. Then we'll see who has autism!

On that train journey, I began reading accounts of late or adult diagnoses and I found them very relatable. Previously I had only read accounts by men who were diagnosed sometimes as early as seven, which were completely unrelatable to me. Generally, the late diagnosis accounts that I found more relatable were from women. Due to societal factors like sexism or medical misogyny, women don't generally get early diagnoses except in more extreme cases. A surprising number of medical professionals still believe that spectrum disorders are more prevalent in boys and will wave away girls on this basis, letting evidence fit their presumptions. For example, if a boy gets obsessed with train schedules, he'll get prodded by medics, but if a girl is obsessed with horses to the same degree, she won't. Girls also have higher social pressure to conform, which leads to better masking (hiding your autism through learned behaviour). Boys are freer to behave as they like and so the autistic behaviour pops out and can be seen and quantified. (Autism has been said to present differently in women, even at a physical level in the brain,[4] so much so that male and female autistic brains can be distinguished from each other in a way that non-autistic male and female brains cannot, though this is currently being disputed.)

We are still unpicking nature from nurture when it comes to neurodivergence and I recommend reading accounts from people whose demographics don't match your own. I found reading outside of my 'group' especially valuable because, as someone who is excellent at masking (hiding my autism through changing my behaviour) – certainly good enough to

4 *The British Journal of Psychiatry* , Volume 220, Special Issue 4: Themed Issue: Precision Medicine and Personalised Healthcare in Psychiatry, June 2022, pp. 202–209 DOI: https://doi.org/10.1192/bjp.2022.13

make it in live comedy and avoid diagnosis for thirty years – I related to late-diagnosed female accounts far more. It had never occurred to me that consciously monitoring my body language or facial expression during conversation was unusual or that most people didn't use tricks to make eye contact easier. Who knew that it was unusual to have spent a lot of time watching people's public behaviour and reading articles or books about socialising in order to learn how to do it? Like, say, an alien? Pretty much everyone, it turned out, but it was news to me. Suffice to say, I emerged onto the concourse at Paddington Station a shaken man.

I arrived home and said to my partner, 'You know, I think I might be on the spectrum' and she reacted as if I'd just burst in, jabbed my fingers at my chest and said, 'I think these might be nipples'. I would say 'Duh' is a concise approximation of her response and it was, in its own way, reassuring. It's not always the response one wants, though. I'd have been fine with some version of 'You? The glowing socialite? The man they banned from the Caribbean for being too relaxed? British eye-contact champion ten years running? Fye! Nonsense! I'll have any doctor who confirms it struck off!' But there you go. We are who we are.

Normally, a heckle is followed by a put-down. This heckle was followed by months of introspection, questionnaires, appointments and, eventually, a diagnosis. As is often the case with medical issues, especially with matters of mental health or the brain, once you really start researching it you realise how terrifyingly shallow our knowledge is. We know so little about how the brain works and why. We take what little we know and then misapply it using biased, out-of-date or cultural metrics, further distorting the image. Fortunately for all of us, lots of very clever and motivated people are working on that sort of thing, at least until their funding is cut, so I'll stick to what I do best: communicating with the public in an amusing way.

Maybe you picked up this book because you never felt you could ask 'Why can't I just enjoy things?' out loud. Maybe you've never asked the question for fear of seeming like a miserable shit or revealing how measurable a gulf there is between you and the 'normal majority of people', with their baffling, incomprehensible behaviour. Maybe the title reminded you of someone you know. Then again, maybe the question struck you as so bizarre you felt compelled to see what I was on about.

I wouldn't force anyone to get a diagnosis, and even if I tried, there is often a years-long waiting list if you can't afford private care. However, I suspect that far, far more people meet the threshold for autism than we would ever have imagined. It certainly seems likely that there are more of us out there, judging by the unsettled reactions of friends when they hear about my diagnosis and they ponder how much we have in common, or when I let someone fill in a questionnaire for a laugh and they score high, in some cases even higher than me, to say nothing of the ever-growing trickle of celebrities 'coming out' as diagnosed. I'd love to reach the silent autistic people hiding in plain sight, if only because I can personally attest to how much their lives will improve when they have a good answer to that terrible question that's followed them for as long as they can remember:

Why can't I just enjoy things?

CHAPTER 1

Why Should I Bother Getting Diagnosed?

During the process of my diagnosis, by far the most common question I was asked by friends, family and colleagues was something along the lines of, 'Well, if it's who you are, and nothing can be done about it, and your life seems pretty good, why bother?' Or, more simply, 'What will it *change*?'

I suppose partly they were asking this because of how well I mask my problems or how high-functioning I seem. Some of them were reacting like I was in too much of a rush – woah, slow down, buddy! Where's the autistic fire?! And to be fair to them, my biggest issues as an autistic adult were mostly private or easy to explain away. However, they were also onto something crucial: your diagnosis is just confirmation of something immutable about you.

WHY CAN'T I JUST ENJOY THINGS?

You are autistic, that is that. It is who you are.[5] We are not talking about the glasses through which you see the world, we are talking about your eyeballs, your brain. It is very important *and* extremely difficult to accept this, or at least it was for me, but it is true.

The more I perform comedy about my diagnosis or reference my new-found status as autistic, the more I see people in the crowd being nudged or nodding and looking unsettled, like I'm onstage describing a dream that they've also somehow had. I get messages on social media from people saying that my show has made them interested in getting diagnosed, or that they are now looking into it. These are generally accompanied by questions about the resources I used and recommend. I love these messages because they show that the stand-up routine is accomplishing something I wanted it to, and one of the things I always get from stand-up and which I love: a feeling of solidarity with a stranger. A feeling of being seen and known and having private things expressed by someone else in a public forum and having them accepted. Plus, maybe I am helping these people in their quest to understand themselves better.

The reason I love responding to all these messages is because, in short, I believe that it is worth it to be diagnosed. (Even if you keep it entirely to yourself which, I must stress, is an option!) It's worth it because it is an unchangeable fact

---

5   People like to say that autism, or being ginger, or being Spanish doesn't 'define' them. They mean that they don't like to imagine it limiting them, or limiting the way they are seen by others. Of course your qualities define you to some extent – they determine who and how you are and why. That's not a moral judgement, it's just true. You don't have to let that limit you and if someone wants to think of you in a simplistic way, there is little you can do to stop them.

about who you are and, I would say, you will never fully understand yourself or your life without investigating it in some form.

Some people take this immutable fact and use it to justify inaction, which is their decision. They say, 'Well, if I already have it and there's no cure, why bother? Why do these differences need pointing out, or diagnosing? Can't we just get on with our lives and tolerate each other?' Well, if you are wondering if people can just get along with each other in tolerance and peace, I encourage you to read the news and then decide for yourself. It's also about whether or not *you*, the patient, give a shit. If you're happy, we're happy. If you're not distressed, great. If you feel that your condition, whatever it may or may not be, is not stopping you from living your life in the way that you want to live it, then that's great news. That said, I would argue that, like me when I was undiagnosed autistic but still suffering the setbacks associated with autism, you may be unaware of the ways in which you are being limited, or taking risks, or losing out on help, so maybe it's worth taking a look anyway. You don't know what you don't know.

However, I cannot deny that there are some instances where you would be right not to get diagnosed. Let's say you live in a country where medical records are insecure, or where it's hard to keep them private in a professional context. Maybe you are in a society where autism is incorrectly classified as a mental illness, or misunderstood as automatically signifying an inability to function, or as a severe disability regardless of your individual circumstances. Maybe you're worried that it will be used against you professionally, or personally, maybe everyone you know is an arsehole. These are all circumstances where discretion and even wilful ignorance may be preferable. However, I think it is worth acknowledging that these circumstances are negative circumstances. They are not equally valid alternate systems, they're incorrect, morally and scientifically, and in an ideal world would not exist. Unfortunately, I won't be able to offer much helpful advice for these situations. I am fortunate in that in the United Kingdom, at least so far, there is good progress being made regarding neurodivergent acceptance and a pre-existing social acceptance, or tolerance, for the neurodivergent, compared to many other countries.[6]

These serious exceptions aside, it seems a lot of the underlying motivation to avoid diagnosis is fear and shame. It is not nice, especially if you are already a largely functioning adult, to have to confront new and/or unchangeable difficulties. This is where the privacy option comes in – you are under no obligation to inform your employer, colleagues, friends, family or loved ones if you get diagnosed. I mean, I would, and have, but you don't have to if you don't feel like it.

For the first few months after my diagnosis, I was seized by a terrible urge to tell almost everyone I met, almost everyone I spoke to – it felt quasi-religious. It must be how it feels to become vegan, or to sign up to run a marathon. I felt almost as though if I told people, I would be understood better or

---

6 The British love of eccentrics has something to do with this, I think. People from the UK generally underestimate how unusual and lovely it is to have a country where a weird guy who reads incredibly niche books and inevitably has ketchup on his trousers is regarded with affection and not as a useless freak. I don't know how many other nations would have made the television shows *University Challenge*, *QI* or *Only Connect*, or God knows how many bizarre and fiddly gameshows on BBC Radio 4.

maybe that some sort of vaguely positive reaction would occur. However, there are still social risks to telling people, as I discovered. Most people were nice about it, or faintly interested the way one might be about an acquaintance's pet, but this is still the UK. British people do not enjoy *hearing about* psychiatric matters – if you are eccentric we'd rather not know *why*. A few people, even close friends, reacted as though I was excitedly telling them I had found a new way to wipe my arse. Pleased for me, but slightly unsettled and ultimately unsure as to why I felt the need to tell them. A few were even openly sceptical of the diagnosis, which initially irritated me, but I quickly realised was down to masking my autism so well. Ultimately, it was a kind of compliment on my masking skills. Also, as I will point out again and again throughout this book, non-autistic people love to indirectly request reassurance by saying negative things about themselves. Given that, these people were performing the correct social response by downplaying my concerns and trying to cast doubt on what I had said about myself, as though they were saying 'Awww, you're not fat!'. Apparently, some people find compliments that you have forced someone to give you through guilt reassuring!

After a few months, though, I realised that there was value in withholding my diagnosis from people until it was relevant. It meant that I could stay in control of the information and could have more control of how I was perceived, which in some situations is invaluable. For example, if I knew I was dealing with someone who would not have a positive or accurate reaction to autism.

I will also admit here a degree of self-interest. There

is strength in numbers, after all, and the estimates of the prevalence of autism in the population used to be about 1 per cent. More recent estimates, especially now that Asperger's has been folded into autism (more on this later), are around 3 per cent. Even these numbers only encompass those cases that are profound enough to be noticed in childhood when looked for – they would not count, for example, me. If we also factor in the socio-economic factors and cultural factors that reduce diagnosis,[7] well, hell, let's call it 5 per cent! That'll include all the people I meet who tell me that, yes, of course they *know*, they just don't feel the need to get it on their medical record. A new study by UCL indicates that the number of autistic people in England may be twice as high as previously thought.[8]

I believe that if everyone who could get diagnosed did get diagnosed, or at the very least was 'socially' diagnosed, i.e. was aware of it, talked to their family and friends about it, we would transform the understanding of autism in this country and immediately create pressure and willingness to help or make reasonable adjustments for the people in our lives with autism. Put simply, if you realise that your cousin has autism and have some informative chats with them, you will be kinder to the autistic person at work. That's my self-interest declared, and my semi-utilitarian argument for diagnosis at the same time. Join your local Autistic Union today! If we went on strike, we would cripple the STEM industries,

7 Working-class people, women and people of colour are significantly underdiagnosed. Am J Public Health. 2009 March; 99(3): 493–498. DOI: 10.2105/AJPH.2007.131243 J Autism Dev Disord. 2018 May; 48(5): 1698–1711. DOI: 10.1007/s10803-017-3413-9

8 https://www.ucl.ac.uk/news/2023/jun/number-autistic-people-england-may-be-twice-high-previously-thought

bare minimum, to say nothing of the fantasy role-playing games industry.

Is autism a disability?

Essentially, yes. Autism is a developmental disability; you have it for your whole life and it affects how you interact with the world around you and other people. However, especially among people with low support needs like me, this can be a controversial view. Some of us argue that we simply have a different neurotype to the majority, that we are neurodivergent and not neurotypical. We argue that we are simply 'freshwater fish in salt water. Put us in fresh water and we function just fine. Put us in salt water and we struggle to survive.'[9] Or, in other words, the disability part is created by context, by society, and is a matter of perspective.

The trouble with this is that it is a privileged point of view – what about autistic people who are non-verbal? These are tangibly disabling things with or without neurotypical context. However, if people start talking about 'curing' these things or 'curing' autism generally, it sounds to people like me like unnecessary eugenics talk. I like who I am! I don't want to be cured and I find the idea of someone 'curing' me out of existence very creepy and supervillain-y. (You might ask: well, what about those with co-occurring conditions like seizures? Severe gastro-intestinal trouble? Those conditions are co-occurring with autism but they are

---

9   As told to Baron-Cohen by an autistic person. Baron-Cohen, S. (2003). *The Essential Difference: Male and female brains and the truth about autism.* New York: Basic Books, p.181.

not autism itself – we need to work on dealing with seizures and severe gastro-intestinal issues whoever is suffering from them.)

Then again, I am privileged because (while I do have my issues) my autism is generally easier to deal with than others: I can communicate verbally, I don't have meltdowns where I injure myself or others, I am every inch the 'high functioning' stereotype that neurotypicals prefer to imagine. I find Simon Baron-Cohen's argument convincing – he says some aspects are 'differences' and some are 'disabilities' and both camps can get along just fine.

Legally, away from the moral and philosophical debate, it *can* count as a disability in the UK if you have a physical or mental impairment and the impairment has a substantial and long-term adverse affect on your ability to carry out normal day-to-day activities. The law is concerned more with *need* and *obligation* than with ideal scenarios or wants and, as a result, is dependent on interpretation. I am autistic but I don't mind fluorescent lighting, so I am not impaired from working in an office with that lighting. However, many autistic people find the visual effect, the flicker and the sound of fluorescent lighting utterly intolerable, so they would be impaired. It's all relative and, as ever, dependent on the quality of your lawyer and the size of your wallet. So, legally, I'd say the answer is 'probably', but, if I use myself as an example, my autism workplace requirements would be: I need clear, unambiguous instructions. If I fucked up a job because my employer failed to provide clear instructions, I'd have to argue and convince a tribunal or court of that fact. Not necessarily an easy thing to do. Then again, lawyers are just as pedantic about language as autistic people, so perhaps I'd be preaching to the choir.

Due to the negative feelings people have for the word 'disability' and the 'high functioning' and savant or savant-like effects of some people's autism, you hear a lot of well-intentioned rhetoric about how autism can be a superpower. While that is lovely, it makes all the autistic people who *aren't* Albert Einstein feel like donkey-brained losers and it means that the ones who *are* like Albert Einstein feel obliged to play down the enormous difficulties they face in their personal lives, or to see those difficulties as part of some Faustian pact made on their behalf. As though Mephistopheles took their parents aside and said, 'Your kid is going to be socially miserable, suffer with panic attacks at parties, no eye contact, a decent amount of bullying, *BUT* ... they will end up with a Nobel Prize. Deal?' Whereas in reality, much of the misery of autism is caused by society's structure, its expectations or people's attitudes and is, therefore, optional. So, while pleasant for some, the 'autism is a superpower' rhetoric can cause more harm than good.

So, caveats addressed, why is it still worth getting diagnosed?

Ever since I was young, I was aware of holes in my understanding of who I was, my abilities and my limitations. I knew that there were some things I could do that others could not and some things I found impossible that everyone else found easy. My dad remembers me asking him in a fit of frustration, 'Why do I feel so different to the other kids?' when I was primary-school age. My father, who I think had similar feelings when he was young, told me that the reason

I felt different was because I was different and that I had better get used to the idea. Good advice! Autism diagnoses rarely come as a surprise in the sense that the recipient didn't perceive anything different about themselves; they tend to come as a surprise only in that the recipient didn't expect autism to be the answer.[10]

Over the years, I toyed with various explanations and other diagnoses but none of them covered all the problem areas or answered every query, only ever some of them. The duvet of knowledge was too small for the mattress of inquiry! It was only once I started properly researching autism that I realised I had a solution in front of me for every question I'd ever had about myself, about why I was different. At last, a duvet that fitted the bed.

I am a firm believer in the maxim 'know thyself'. If you know yourself, understand your limitations and your needs, you can lead a better, more fulfilled life. I also believe that the unexamined life is not worth living. Well, to be fair, if you are living an unexamined life and absolutely loving it, like a pig in shit, then go for it. Enjoy! But if you are leading an unexamined life and experiencing intermittent agonies of confusion and doubt, or inexplicable personal problems that prod you in the head at 3 a.m. like a bored cat, then maybe start examining that life of yours.

Thanks to my diagnosis I am aware that, for example, my hatred of small sounds is just something that I should expect to happen to me. It's just something that I have, and that's that. It's not a personal failing, it's not a moral failing, it

---

10 Like myself! Due to my ignorance of autism, I would never have thought it could ever apply to me.

just *is a thing*. It's also, crucially, not the fault of the person making the small sounds. It's not a personal or moral failing on their part either. Well, probably not ... I can reconcile my personal opinion that if you chew with your mouth open you have failed as an adult with my philosophical belief that this is not an objective truth, but fuck me ... it's a struggle to stay philosophical when you animals are smashing crisps with your mouths open right next to me on the train. The diagnosis has made it far easier to feel Zen about my tedious autistic suffering, to be mindful of how irritated some things make me but not let that irritation become too 'real' or overwhelming or ruin my day.

However, that does bring me on to something that will happen if you get diagnosed. You will gain certainty and lose hope. You are becoming personally correct but wrong in the majority. I was always aware of the various things 'wrong' with me and my inexplicable failings (of which more later on in this book. Well, OK, pretty much every chapter), but I always carefully nursed the idea that these failings were solvable and I could fix myself. If I could only, somehow, achieve the optimum routine, amount of sleep, amount of exercise! If I could somehow magic up the right kind of self-discipline, maybe take multivitamins, then I would finally be a 'proper' person. To an extent this is true, especially for young men: you will go from being a weird slob in your early twenties to a neater, tidier person in your thirties – a fluent user of fabric softener, a vacuumer of crumbs. However, I didn't realise that I was working with a limited energy budget, that I only had so much energy for so many things and that sometimes the second I put energy into, say, finally organising my exercise routines and eating well, I would lose energy for something else. Nevertheless, I was raised, perhaps like you, to believe that it was simply a matter of sorting yourself out, getting things done, getting organised. I took these failings personally and that created a lot of unnecessary unhappiness and stress which, oho, demotivates you and saps your energy, making the problem worse. Well done, brain.

With a diagnosis, I have what you might call an official reason to be kinder to myself. A sick note for the PE lesson of my unreasonable expectations. I can also take my limitations more seriously after a lifetime of having them dismissed, of having people tell me that these limitations were either laziness or a figment of my imagination, which I fully believed. Now, if I know that my routine is about to be seriously disrupted for a few days, I can plan for that and for my negative reaction to it. I can override my desire to be amenable and agree to things to seem like a Good Guy Who Is Up For Stuff and feel better about saying, 'Sorry, I can't!' or just cancelling. This might all seem like simple stuff, but it was a revelation for me and has definitely reduced my exhaustion, stress or periods of burnout.

However, as I said above, you do lose hope in exchange for these certainties. I have lost the hope, for example, that there really was a solution all along. I no longer have the belief that someday I will 'fix' myself fully, that I will become this mystical Proper Person and manage to enjoy all the things I should have been enjoying all along. I'd finally fit in socially as seamlessly and painlessly as a fish in a shoal, instead of always feeling like an umpire at an orgy: removed from the action and trying to keep track of everything while other people have fun. Even though that hope was entirely in vain (the diagnosis didn't *give* me autism – after all, I had it all along), it was still a nice idea and a good motivator for self-improvement *towards* that goal, if never quite reaching it. If you were in prison, would you rather have the false dream of someday being released or the knowledge that you would never be, and therefore make the most of the life you have within those walls? That probably won't win Most Cheerful Analogy of the Year but I think it's a useful framing for figuring out how you feel about hope as an idea.

Some of you reading this will be thinking, 'But this is just true for everyone! No one is always on top of everything!', in which case let me do my best to illustrate the greater seriousness of what I am talking about. You are right that this sort of thing is notionally true for most people,[11] but when I say that I was lacking as a Proper Person, I mean more that, depending on how tired I was, or how poorly I had planned my diary, I could end up not cooking for myself for weeks at a time, I could end up not budgeting time for sleep over a three-day period, or attempting to do something professional or social every evening for a month and burning myself out completely, or agreeing to do an enormous amount of work for free out of a desire to be helpful and a misplaced sense of social obligation that didn't even exist. It is not normal to become so irritated by your inability to actually use up all of that pasta you bought that you decide to eat a kilogram of pasta, for example. But it is certainly logical – the pasta has

---

11 Or maybe you are autistic, too! I spent years reading the complaints of possibly autistic or actually autistic people and thinking, 'Oh, come on, that's just normal.' Nope. Turns out it's not.

been used and all in such a time-efficient manner! And once it's gone, it won't annoy us anymore! That's the sort of thing I am talking about, to give some examples off the top of my head, but everyone will have their own.

The self-knowledge gained by the diagnosis means I can stop and say to myself, 'Am I really going to prepare and eat all of these stir-fry vegetables? Or do I merely wish that I was the sort of person who *would*? Let's be honest with ourselves here, just get one packet, not seven in the vain hope that the visible waste of six packets of stir-fry vegetables will somehow compel you to use them. Remember the Great Cabbage Waste of lockdown? Exactly.' It means that if I am exhausted by gigging or writing or socialising, I can eat something simple or bad and not haul myself over the coals for it. It means I can take myself and my limitations more seriously.

This brings me on to the latter part of what I said above: you will become personally correct and wrong in the eyes of the majority.

You will realise that you have a really good reason for being utterly furious at someone for making small noises, or a really good reason for being obsessed with something and unable to convince people that it's interesting. However, finding out that you are in a specialised 1 to 5 per cent of the population, in brain terms, means that you, your instincts and opinions are *wrong for the majority*. Statistically speaking, most people are not like you. Now, obviously this is true for many people, but they have the luxury of never having to confront that truth. They can sit around imagining the glorious silent majority that agrees with them. They can picture that they are, broadly, a Normal and Reasonable Person, a Fine Citizen, that they have the Correct, True Opinion on all matters, both weighty and whimsical. They may or may not be right, but it doesn't matter: they get to think it, or at least consider it possible. I remember genuinely thinking, when it came to some of my autistic loves or hates, that there was a decent chance most people were actually like me. In the case of some of the more niche ones, I was realistic enough to think 'OK, perhaps not everyone wants to pull out their own eyes in fury when someone says "brekkie", but hey, I'm sure it's still a healthy one fifth of people. Maybe?'

Sadly, no. I have come to accept that at a literal neurological level, I am not the same as at least 90 per cent of people. They don't have words or sounds that fill them with fury, they don't communicate literally, they don't get so obsessed by things that they forget to eat and drink, and they never will. That doesn't matter really, but it does feel like a lonelier world since I became more aware of how profound these barriers to communication and mutual understanding are, and how real these differences can be. The terrible certainty of solid facts. Certainty is like a castle wall: it can be reassuring and protective, or imprisoning and isolating, depending on your perspective.[12]

I mentioned earlier the various risks of disclosing your diagnosis, the situations some people face where diagnosis could be genuinely dangerous, so I should also mention the sort of situations where the disclosure can be invaluable.

I should say at this point that, if formal medical diagnosis is either unavailable or unaffordable for you, then self-diagnosis

---

12 Sometimes I wish I only spoke once a week and it was to say things like this before returning to my forge.

can be a legitimate option. It can be risky, but to be frank, once I had done months of obsessively autistic research into autism I was so certain I had it that by the time I met with medical professionals, I was terrified they would tell me I *didn't* have it and deprive me of all these perfect answers to my many questions. I was terrified they would say, 'Nope, says here you're just a cunt!' and force me to start the process of figuring myself out from scratch.

If you feel you are certain you have it, or think you might, you can get a huge amount of value in reading all the same literature that I have, the same blogs and books and studies, in order to further understand yourself and your condition. It will be harder to justify to the outside world but it will be just the same to you personally, inside your head, especially if you are not in a position to feel it necessary to explain yourself to others. If so, good luck to you, but if it's possible to get a piece of paper from a medical authority it can be a game-changer. It could give you the power to formally or legally request adjustments, understanding or assistance from your employer, from your healthcare provider or even from the state.

For example, years ago and, crucially, pre-diagnosis, I was doing some writing for a television show. Autistic people can struggle with employment due to the difficulties they face from their environment or from unaware or unsympathetic employers. Only 22 per cent of autistic adults are in any kind of employment,[13] though remember this definition includes autistic people with additional learning disabilities. My

---

13 Office for National Statistics, 'Outcomes for disabled people in the UK: 2021'. https://www.ons.gov.uk/peoplepopulationandcommunity/healthandsocialcare/disability/articles/outcomesfordisabledpeopleintheuk/2021

solution, it turns out, was to be self-employed as a comedian. However, even in comedy there are times when what you are doing is sitting in an office and typing on a computer as part of a team with a boss. I always knew that I did best with clear instructions, even pre-diagnosis. Unfortunately, it seems that, no matter how many times you tell some people that you *need* direct instructions, they simply won't give them to you.

They'll say that they understand, they'll always agree that clear, direct instructions are best. But they are only agreeing because it's a sort of rhetorical obviousness, a kind of trap. After all, who's going to say that they prefer vague communication? Who thinks that they'd prefer confusing instructions? The person in charge of me and my writing on this particular day was one of these people: they never directly said what they wanted, they never said what they meant and they seemed hell-bent on refusing to admit that they were in charge. They seemed to find their power over people icky in some way, like someone embarrassed to have hired a cleaner. I found them baffling. They would heavily suggest that I might *consider*, if I *wanted to*, writing something about a particular topic, while repeatedly emphasising that it was up to me, and repeatedly emphasising how good my writing was anyway, and various other vague and positive statements. When I tried to ask if the topic was what they *wanted* me to write on, they recoiled in horror at the idea that they would ever order me to do something, shocked at the suggestion they were prescribing topics. I found it very frustrating that someone who was clearly literally in charge would behave like this. I did my best to clarify my instructions but to no avail.

In this situation, I made a classic autistic mistake: taking someone literally. I had become so exhausted by trying to solve this little social riddle, so paralysed by my inability to figure out what the 'correct' thing to do was, that I just decided it was safe to take this person at their word. At least then I could say, 'Well, you told me it was OK.' Big mistake. What this person wanted was for me to do as they said and also to *still like them*, or not resent them for being in charge, and for me to feel complimented and clever while I followed orders.[14] Instead, what they got was me taking them at their word: I wrote about what I wanted to write about and, naturally, they told me how wonderful it was, because that's how they operated. Sadly, I didn't last much longer in that job! That boss was so annoyed I hadn't followed their implied orders that they ghosted me and my agent for weeks and stopped telling me when to come in for work. After weeks of this, during which I was supposed to be working for them, they finally responded and tried to claim non-completion of work via my agent. When it was pointed out to them that I had done all the work I had been told to do, and even done extra work for others for free when we were short-staffed, they admitted it just hadn't worked out and paid my fee in full.

Bizarre behaviour but not uncommon and, the childish ghosting aside, I think looking back, I can sort of understand it. This boss was behaving, as far as they were concerned, like some sort of marvellous flattering and generous king, and

---

14 I find this sort of people management a little pathetic, frankly – don't become a boss if you hate telling people what to do. It is important, even when trying to carve out a space for yourself and your needs, to recognise when some businesses are just inherently unfriendly to autistics by their nature and also to admit the utility of those unfriendly behaviours. For example, this person would have been an amazing boss for an egomaniac creative who needed greasing! Right job, wrong tool, or vice versa.

I had rudely ignored their kindness. I was a peasant in the snow and I was telling Good King Wenceslas to shove his flesh and wine up his arse. It would never have occurred to this person that I would have preferred a gun-to-the-head set of demands from them, rather than this unsettling rub-your-shoulders-and-feed-you-Turkish-delight approach. In this case, I was extremely fortunate to have good representation in the form of my agent who fought my corner, but many autistic employees, diagnosed or not, have no such luck. If I had been diagnosed and been able to communicate it to this person, things might have been different.

Can I guarantee that such a person would have been able to sufficiently comprehend the diagnosis in such a way that they adjusted their behaviour? Can I be sure such a person is even able to adjust their behaviour? No, in all honesty, I cannot guarantee it – but there is a chance! Hope springs eternal and you never know until you try. I can certainly guarantee that this person wouldn't, and didn't, make any adjustments *without* a diagnosis waved in their face, so having something to wave in their face has to be better than nothing. It's also important to mention that, once disclosed, your employer has a *legal obligation* to make reasonable adjustments for you, and so at least you have recourse if they fail to do so. This means that even if this person is an awful bastard who thinks neurodivergence is just an excuse for laziness, they can at least be threatened into behaving themselves.

Often the sheer seriousness of waggling a doctor's note in someone's face is enough to spook them into taking you seriously, so it can be worth getting diagnosed if only to have something to waggle. How else will you convince your busy, maybe wilfully ignorant employer to finally install non-buzzing lighting? To let you work from home one a day week to avoid a meltdown? Get your piece of paper, make sure all correspondence is in written form, keep copies and remember that HR works for the company first and you second. If I'd had my piece of paper, I could possibly have spent longer living my dream and working for a brilliant show instead of needlessly going through a drawn-out, embarrassing tussle with a former boss and losing a chance to be part of something great.

None of this would have been necessary in a world where people communicate literally but, unfortunately, they don't. None of this forcing compassion using medical notes would be necessary in a world where people were willing or able to spend time and energy understanding one another but, again, they often aren't. That much is self-evident in this case. Given that, having a legally significant piece of paper could be invaluable. It's a shame that it has to come to that, but clearly it must.

That brings me to another factor in my self-interest in getting everyone either diagnosed or talking seriously about the reasonable adjustments that neurodivergent people might need – it will make all of our lives easier. Every new diagnosis issued, every new adjustment requested, strengthens the argument of the next person to get a diagnosis or make a request. Once you get your diagnosis, you get a far better awareness of your needs but confirmation that your needs are the needs of a minority. We need to stick together – if neurotypical people were able to take us seriously, to accommodate us without being made to, they would have done so already.

Personally speaking, as opposed to this sort of philosophical, legal, social approach, my view on my own diagnosis is more complex, I'm afraid. Theory is all very well until it smacks into the terrible meat of real life.

I was once asked if, having been diagnosed at thirty-one, I wished I had been diagnosed earlier. It's a very difficult question. As with any alternative history question, the second you start changing this one thing or that one thing, you find you must change other things for the whole scenario to still make sense. I have decided that I wish I had been diagnosed at eighteen years old, on balance. Even then, I'm not certain. I am biased because my life has gone well so far, so it feels insincere or even greedy to imagine that either I could have had an *even better* life than I have had, or that I deserve *even more nice* things in my life, having already had quite a few.

I am also lucky to have open-minded and kind parents, so when I contemplate something like a childhood diagnosis I can easily imagine the best version of it. I don't have to worry about whether or not my parents would have denied me a diagnosis, or accepted it and used it as a reason to abandon all hope for me, or allowed some unsympathetic or incompetent doctor or teacher to recommend all the wrong treatments, attitudes, therapies. Even now there are plenty of people in positions of power like medical professionals or teachers with attitudes to autism more suited to *One Flew Over the Cuckoo's Nest* than to the modern world, so if I didn't have the parents I have, I'd be giving a different answer.

As you will read later in the book, I found elements of university extremely difficult, and in the years between eighteen and my diagnosis at thirty-one there were several personal and professional moments where the self-knowledge of my diagnosis and my ability to explain myself to others would have been invaluable. Just last night, at the time of writing, I chatted to a man in Bristol after a tour show who has an autistic wife and child. He said that the diagnosis isn't really for you, it's for the people around you; to help them understand you, to help them help you, and that's a very good point indeed. I would have found a lot of relationships easier to navigate if I had been in possession of an official piece of paper that said, 'You really should take me literally' or 'It's not personal, or a bad sign, or anything to do with you actually, that I need alone time.' I could have planned and executed my studies during university in a less insane manner, maybe got some official help from the university or, more likely, some unofficial help in the form of compassion and understanding from staff. I could have had more protection from the challenges of a new environment.

But if what we are after is help, protection and awareness, why not get diagnosed even younger? Well, there we run into an issue. Between the ages of eleven and eighteen I taught myself how to socialise, how to mask my autism (a useful skill to have, regardless of whether or not one 'should have to' mask) and how to rub along with others. During that time, I unlocked my sense of humour, learned how to share it with people and, in doing so, made lifelong friends. However, I also masked too much, losing some of my sense of self, and ended up overeating as a sort of stress-compensation, so there were certainly downsides.[15]

---

15 I used to look like a slim swimmer-type person! I cannot believe, looking back, that I thought I wasn't in great shape. Normally it's women saying that sort of thing and hearing about body image issues from me makes men in audiences annoyed or uncomfortable – maybe it seems too feminine to them for a big hairy man to say, I don't know, but more of that later in the chapter that deals with food.

WHY SHOULD I BOTHER GETTING DIAGNOSED?

At certain points, I would gladly have welcomed a diagnosis if it meant an end to the seemingly constant social confusion and suffering. It is not comfortable to admit but now that those years of strain and suffering are over, I am glad I did them. It was total agony at the time but, for good or for ill, made me who I am today. Maybe I am behaving like one of those toxic 1950s types who, desperate to not undermine their sense of self, ends up subconsciously justifying their own severe beatings at the hands of sadistic Edwardians, but I do think there was tremendous value in it, *given that I survived it.* It was like some sort of sadistic fitness regimen.

In all honesty, I am having to unlearn a lot of what I learned. Or rather learn the difference between things I like doing and things I do automatically to seem normal.[16] Then again, as human beings, we are all ongoing projects – maybe by the time you read this I will have fully dismantled my entire sense of self from those years and gone back to being a near-silent, antisocial monk. For now, though, the skills I gained through that suffering are crucial in my daily, personal and professional life, so can I honestly regret the suffering? Then again, can I truly recommend suffering to other blameless children when it could easily have broken me or ended badly instead of well? When it was essentially a survival response to a harsh environment that *didn't need to be that harsh*?

That's the rub. Your opinion on the value of the suffering will entirely hinge around how you answer the following question: Do you believe it is possible to create, consistently across all

---

16   In the weeks or months after your diagnosis, you will begin to consciously or unconsciously stop masking in a way that can seem quite dramatic, so watch out for that. More on that in Chapter 3.

of society, an environment so much nicer, so considerate, that autistic people can be themselves, wholly? I'm afraid that I don't quite believe that it is possible. It feels too utopian, like never teaching people self-defence and instead just agitating for 'an end to violent people'. A nice idea, but generally violent people are unaware, unable or unwilling to fix themselves, or violent out of reflex or passion and not pre-planned intent. So, maybe we do try to help them but we also teach everyone how to defend themselves.

I'm not a total pessimist! I would say we could get people and society to be so considerate of autism, to set up educational or professional environments with such awareness of it, that maybe we could reduce the suffering from a metaphorical 75 per cent to 20 per cent. It's important to be realistic. After all, in the UK at least, we can barely be bothered to fund language learning in schools or assistants for deaf children. To say nothing of attitude or culture problems even *if we had the money*: it would be childish to imagine some magical country where there were no bad teachers and no bad pupils. Still, with some effort, we could achieve something manageable, like maybe schools being more understanding about the intolerable texture of those jumpers they make you wear.

If you believe that a better world is wholly possible, one where autistic kids will *only* benefit from diagnosis, then the best course by far is to diagnose everyone as young as possible and also tell everyone about it. Another key question: Do I think that my social difficulties would have been lessened or magnified by a diagnosis? Quite possibly magnified! And I was at a good school. If you are at a bad school, it may not be worth 'coming out' as autistic. Even in my good school, I could easily imagine one or two teachers using my autism as a reason to write me off, to create an excuse for me to stop trying (which I may have *loved*). Then again, school does not have to control your future, so maybe the long-term benefits of being diagnosed at a young age outweigh the short-term drawbacks of having your autism thrown in your face by bullies.

Overall, I'd say that personally it would have been useful to get my diagnosis at eighteen years old, but I worry that if I had had it between eleven and eighteen, I would have been socially written off and used the diagnosis myself as either an excuse for not trying as hard or, more kindly, a *reason* for not trying as hard. Maybe if I had been diagnosed at, say, seven years old, I would have grown up ignorant of other possibilities and the implicit pressures of normality and instead grown up labelled-but-enabled. Again, we find ourselves in a swamp of hypotheticals and must just shrug and say: well, then again if I had wheels I'd be an autistic bicycle. Never mind alternate realities and the regrets of a lifetime! The thrust of it is this: I wish I had known earlier, I am glad I know now and I think you'll be glad too.

CHAPTER 2

What Happened to Asperger's?

If you're going to understand autism, I'm afraid you're going to need something of a primer on it. It might seem complicated from the outside, it certainly did to me, but once you know the origins of what we are talking about when we say 'autism' it all falls into place quite easily, especially if you enjoy history as much as I do. If not, don't worry. After this, we can return to the sunlit uplands where the amusing anecdotes roam and graze.

If I had been diagnosed as a child, I would have been diagnosed with Asperger's syndrome. However, because I was diagnosed in 2022, I was diagnosed with autism (officially ASD, autism spectrum disorder, but more specifically ASD-1, where 1 is the lowest level of support needed on a scale that goes from 1 to 3, the highest level of support needed).[17] But why the change? Why is it *all* autism now? What happened to Asperger's syndrome?

Well, like all good stories, it involves Nazis and the Second World War.

Before I started researching autism and got diagnosed, I was fairly confident I knew what autism was. I felt I had a passing awareness of its symptoms and effects. Looking back, it is embarrassing how wrong I was. If you are going to fully understand this book you are going to need a brief update on where we stand today regarding autism and a brief lesson in the background or history of autism.

IMPORTANT NOTE: I have discovered, in my research, that there is not a single aspect to psychiatry, psychology, mental health or neurodivergence that isn't incredibly controversial and hotly debated by *someone somewhere*. While this churn of debate is a good thing, it does mean that if you are just a civilian with a diagnosis or chasing a diagnosis, like me, you will get caught in the online crossfire. So, beware the debate. I am aware that I will be crudely simplifying decades of research and I am also aware that not everything I will say is accepted by everyone. That's life, baby! If you don't think I represent your specific experience, I apologise, but how could I ever have done so?

Who tells us what autism is? Where do we get the criteria

---

17 I will say, at this stage, that if it was possible I would put my level of support at like 0.8 if I could. I feel a little like I am exaggerating if I ever say I need 'support', like some heroic war veteran on crutches, but then part of that is the legacy of a lifetime of ignoring and doing down my own concerns in a desperate attempt to fit in. Then again, I also feel the need to be honest with anyone reading who has autism with level 2 or 3 support needs and faces more difficulties than me: I am very aware that life, my functioning in non-autistic society, is much easier for me.

for defining autism? Who decides what counts as autistic or not?

The diagnostic criteria that physicians use is found in something called a diagnostic manual. These are huge, incredibly detailed, peer-reviewed medical textbooks published by large medical organisations to give practitioners the latest definitions, signs and symptoms of various conditions. The United States and much of the world use the DSM or *Diagnostic and Statistical Manual of Mental Disorders*, a manual published by the American Psychiatric Association. In the UK and Europe, however, it is standard to use the World Health Organization's manual, the ICD *or International Classification of Diseases*. These manuals are constantly being debated, revised and republished to ensure they are as accurate and as up to date as possible; at the time of writing, we are on DSM 5 and ICD 11.

OK, so what is autism?

The simple answer is best expressed by the NHS website: autism is not an illness or a disease, it just means your brain works in a different way from other people.[18]

Ah, but how does one get autism? Well, basically, when Bill Gates gives you a vaccine – haha, just kidding. The look on your face!

Autism seems to be something you are born with. It definitely has a strong genetic component, with many parents of diagnosed people displaying signs of autism, although it is not 100 per cent heritable. If you have identical twins and one has autism the other will have autism *almost* but *not*

---

18   https://www.nhs.uk/conditions/autism/what-is-autism/

every time,[19] so there is variability. (In fact, identical twins with autism will have *more* different traits than non-autistic identical twins, so the variability must come from something other than genetics or even home life. Crazy!) If you are autistic, you are autistic forever and ever, amen. There is no cure or treatment for autism itself, though you may require treatments or medication for issues arising from or relating to your autism. For example, you could end up needing antidepressants because of how horribly you are treated for being autistic, but that's more properly society's fault, not autism's fault.

Research into what genes might indicate a predisposition to autism is ongoing and there does seem to be some progress being made in identifying the relevant genes, although our understanding of genes and how they affect people, nature versus nurture, is still in its infancy. Some of the differences between autistic people and non-autistic people seem to be explained by physical differences in the brain, pointing to some sort of developmental difference when the brain is growing that leads to autism to some extent. The general belief is that there are multiple causes that act together. Some people will describe it as something that 'appears' when a child is three or four, but that is simply the stage of growth where it becomes possible to measure a human's development beyond 'shits themselves a lot, loves sucking tits'. That's why it makes a lot more sense, especially with the heritability rate, to assume a genetic aspect and that people are born with it to

19   Castelbaum, L. (2019). 'On the nature of monozygotic twin concordance for autistic trait severity: A quantitative analysis'. *Behavior Genetics.*

some degree. Sometimes symptoms are identifiable enough that people can be diagnosed as infants, sometimes you have to wait until you are a thirty-one-year-old comedian and get heckled in Bristol.

Great, so what's the complicated answer?

I will make a bold attempt to summarise the ICD 11 and DSM 5's description of autism, to avoid simply reprinting it, like a drunk person pulling two people together and insisting they have *loads in common*:

Both manuals describe autism as a neurodevelopmental disorder that is characterised by persistent deficits in the ability to initiate and sustain *reciprocal* social interaction and communication, and by a range of restricted, repetitive and inflexible patterns of behaviour, interests or activities that are *contextually* excessive or atypical. These *contextually* excessive or atypical symptoms are present from early childhood but may not fully manifest until later, depending on the person. These symptoms also limit or impair everyday functioning to some measurable or observable degree.[20] As an added bonus complication, autism is *extremely* heterogeneous. I'll save you from having to look that up like I had to. It means that autism is incredibly varied in its manifestations and that no two people with autism will be the same. This presents a challenge when you are trying to medically define it. This is why, contained under the umbrella of autism, there are various and wide-ranging subtypes or developmental markers. Not to mention all the conditions that seem to be co-occurring with autism,

---

20 ICD-11 for Mortality and Morbidity Statistics, 6A02 Autism Spectrum Disorder, DSM-5 TR F84.0 Autism Spectrum Disorder

ranging from physical conditions that affect the cartilage in your joints to OCD arising as an indirect *result of* your autism.[21]

Basically, if you corner your friends at the age of ten and you all yell at each other about Pokémon without listening, that might be fine, but if you're ten and you corner your friends and force them to listen to twenty minutes of monologue about how air traffic control works, you probably qualify for both the 'lack of reciprocal interaction' *and* the 'narrow interests' at once. Throw in some autistic meltdowns over changes to routine, which is to say a display of 'inflexible or rigid thinking and behaviour', and you're there. I am crudely simplifying here, of course, and context is everything. If you are the son of an air traffic controller or air traffic control is somehow the latest cool fad at school then that would have to be taken into account.

A good example of how perspective defines a problem, issue or difference in mental health is sadness. It is normal to be sad during a funeral. It is not normal to have that level of sadness all day, every day, when no one has died and there is no funeral. That could be depression. It is also generally abnormal to *not* feel sad during a funeral. That could be depression. It's about how far off you are from the bell curve or average of what we see as normal human behaviour. In each chapter of this book, I will do my best to explain, with examples and research, how the signs of autism are justified in being separated out from 'normal' society.

---

21 The list of conditions that autistic people are more likely to have is sobering: Khachadourian, V., Mahjani, B., Sandin, S. *et al.* (2023). 'Comorbidities in autism spectrum disorder and their etiologies'. *Transl Psychiatry* 13, 71. https://doi.org/10.1038/s41398-023-02374-w

Are the diagnostic manuals reliable?

The first thing to clear up is the common misconception that diagnosing conditions, syndromes, mental health disorders, disabilities or whatever is an exact science like diagnosing diabetes or cancer. It is not. There can be a worrying amount of relativism and wiggle room in some diagnostic criteria and, inevitably, culture plays a big part in deciding what is a symptom and what is normal. For example, one of the commonly accepted signs of autism in the West is a lack of eye contact. However, in many other cultures around the world, eye contact is often seen as extremely rude, especially when interacting with someone societally 'above' you. That means that the cultural *opinion* of what constitutes too much or not enough eye contact is not, globally, a reliable indicator. Context is key – eye contact in a job interview is not the same as at the urinals. Without also taking into account culture, religion, gender, sexuality and so on, the manuals won't be of much use – if all we needed were manuals, we wouldn't need people! What *will* be reliable is an individual's sense that eye contact is somehow painful, too intense, or hard to maintain in the same way it's hard to look at a bright light.

There is also a certain amount of inconsistency between practitioners. What is normal to one psychologist is abnormal to another and there are myriad biases with any human being no matter how professional they are. We know so little about the human brain, the human mind. Do not underestimate the amount of debate and churn and change that is constantly happening in these fields. We know more than we ever have, we know more and more every day, but we are far from fully understanding it. It's important that you take these manuals seriously but, at the same time, it's also important that you don't view them as infallible.

Some of the difficulties we face are down to how heterogeneous or highly variable autism is as a condition. It makes it very hard to generalise. As many people are credited with having said: 'If you've met one person with autism, you've met one person with autism.' It's a wide spectrum of different things affecting a wide spectrum of different people with some core features. But what exactly do we mean by spectrum?

We're all on the spectrum, though, aren't we?

People love to say this sort of thing when it comes to autism. I think most neurotypical people are doing it as an attempt to soothe the concerns of a possible or confirmed autistic person, in the same way they'd say someone doesn't look fat. They see autism as bad or, if not outright bad, definitely 'serious', so they don't want you to feel bad by thinking you have it. You'll say that you're autistic or that you have autistic traits and are looking into it and they will say, 'Well, we are all on the spectrum' as a way to simultaneously soothe you, shut down the conversation and, indirectly, dilute the idea of autism into nothing.

People may do this because: they are afraid of autism, they do not understand autism, they do not understand the spectrum as an idea, or all three.

While it's true that autism is a spectrum condition, the idea of everyone being on a spectrum is not what is meant by that word in this context. I am happy to admit that, until I started the process of getting my diagnosis and researching it, I definitely did not understand what was meant by the 'spectrum' part of 'autism spectrum disorder'. I understood the autism spectrum to be a sort of speedometer, like on a car, where the least autistic person was travelling at one kilometre an hour and the most autistic person was hitting speeds of over two hundred kilometres an hour. The needle on this dial just went higher the more autistic you were, and the dial represented everyone in society. I suppose this implies that everyone has some sort of crumb of autism, minimum, to be on the dial, or the spectrum includes zero, so most people are just zero? And then each additional autism point you get moves the needle along until you qualify for Full Autism.

This is not the case.

I'm afraid autism is a spectrum disorder *once you are diagnosed.* The 'spectrum' part of autism spectrum disorder refers to the fact that, once you are officially autistic, your autism can manifest across a wide spectrum of signs and symptoms and change depending on environment. The spectrum is how we explain that two people with autism may not share the same signs of autism. An autistic person can be non-verbal, have serious sensory issues with fluorescent lights and have explosive meltdowns. I don't have any of those signs but I have others that still qualify me as autistic.

The best example from my own life was when I took a test that assesses you for signs of autism. It's called the RAADS-R and, while it's not as precise or sympathetically worded as one would like, it is respected as an accurate test of autistic traits. (Though it is no substitute for an assessment or interviews with a clinician.)

The maximum score is 240. I score about 125 depending

on how you interpret some of the questions. They reckon you start to qualify for an autism assessment or are likely autistic if you get 65 or more. I sent the test to an old friend, who I have always got on very well with, for a laugh (well, it's the sort of thing I enjoy) and he scored in the 170s. I was shocked.

You see, this friend of mine I have known and observed for many years. He has always been very sociable, very popular and part of the main social group of any context (school, university, work, whatever). He's always been very organised, disciplined, healthy and exercising a lot. I knew he and I had some things in common that could be seen as autistic – some special interests, the same issues with other people's social expectations – but nothing dramatic enough to explain this. I wouldn't have been surprised if he had scored around 65, but even higher than me? There's no way. There had to be an explanation – was the test broken?

I asked him to send me his answers so I could try and figure out what the hell had happened. I knew the tests could be inaccurate to an extent, especially without proper guidance as to what the question was getting at in some cases, but not *this* inaccurate. I read through his answers and it became clear: he had incredibly strict ideas and strong feelings about his own routine, changes of plan, things that I am much more ambivalent about. That is what I mean by spectrum: this guy is, day-to-day, far less autistic-seeming than me. You'd never guess it unless you saw how upset he gets if his morning routine is disrupted. It was routine and planning that bumped his score up past mine whereas he scored very low in areas where I scored high. *That* is the spectrum.

The phrase 'we're all on the spectrum' or any of its variations makes no more sense than the closely related nonsense people say about being 'a bit OCD'. These are qualified medical diagnoses and not personality traits. Having low blood sugar might mean you have diabetes, but it might not. It does not mean you 'are a bit diabetic sometimes'.

It's a shame to disabuse people of this in a sense, because often the phrase is used in a way that's intended by neurotypicals to be inclusive. They are trying to say that they empathise and that the person claiming autism shouldn't feel bad. That's very kind, but it does undermine the diagnosis and tell the autistic person that you don't really think they're disabled in any way at all. This could be a problem if they are genuinely trying to explain to you a way in which they are disabled. They could be asking you for help or understanding, or trying to warn you that they might need it in future. You are also accidentally (as was I, in the past) showing this person that you don't actually understand autism and might not be a reliable or sympathetic person if the shit hits the fan.

Generally, it's better to understand autistic people telling you about their autism as akin to someone saying that they are allergic to nuts. It's best to just accept it and deal with the reality of it than to say, 'We're all a bit allergic to nuts, don't feel bad!' and continue thwipping peanuts into your mouth as if everything was fine.

Where attempting to diagnose autism can get a little unnerving is when we start to try to separate cultural opinion from the scientific or medical element of diagnosis. If one person believes that a special guardian spirit lives in their hair and tells them how to avoid traffic, that is a delusional person. If a million people believe that then it's a folk belief and if they write it down, codify it and have meetings about it in a special building once a week, then it is a religion. You cannot diagnose someone with a bad case of religion, much as one may wish to.

This applies to elements of autism as well. It is normal in autism to have a series of special interests or obsessions. That is abnormal purely because people with autism are a small minority of the population. It is worth remembering that if people with autism were 80 per cent of the population, we could be diagnosing neurotypical people with some sort of condition whereby these poor individuals would be deficient by comparison with the autistic majority. I can see the doctor's notes now: 'Patient seems completely unable to form a proper obsession with something! They can't even experience the joy of using their spare time to become a casual expert in a niche topic! We've tried everything, suggesting interesting areas, medication, but these poor people just seem to be lacking something ...'

One of the big issues is that the diagnostic manuals naturally reflect the prevailing culture and presumptions of where they are put together and published. If we travel back in time, we can find some 'mental disorders' that seem controversial to diagnose these days, mental disorders like homosexuality, or hysteria in women. Very much the result of a bunch of Edwardian doctors with white hair jutting from their ears compiling the manual between rounds of golf, that sort of thing. The original DSM, published in 1952, had homosexuality as a 'sociopathic personality disturbance'[22] and

22 '"Gay Is Good": History of Homosexuality in the DSM and Modern Psychiatry', *American Journal of Psychiatry*, Resident's Journal, Volume 18, Issue 1, pp.4–5.

was included on the basis that it was caused by a traumatic parent-child relationship that made you fear the opposite sex. This was debunked by a psychologist called Evelyn Hooker in 1956, but homosexuality remained in the DSM until as late as 1974.[23]

The terms used are changed and dropped, too. For example, the word 'neurosis' is no longer officially used in the DSM or the ICD. Even words like 'idiot' were once official medical diagnoses that you could receive. These days you'd be pretty devastated if you received an official letter from your GP explaining that you were an idiot; however, it would have no *medical* authority. The point I am making is that these are highly intelligent, highly motivated people who are doing their best, but they are still just people and people make mistakes, people are trapped by their contexts. It's important to accept that everything we think we know now about autism can, and probably *should*, change.

To that end, let's dive into why we don't call it Asperger's syndrome anymore.

Why no more Asperger's?

Ever since the DSM-5 came out in 2013 it has been rare or, clinically speaking, inaccurate to get a diagnosis of Asperger's syndrome. Some of the facts and history around this change are societal and some are more science-based. We are going to need a small history lesson to explain this.

---

23   It might seem silly that something so obviously wrong to us needed to be 'debunked' but there you are. Scientific studies are a powerful way to contradict a wrong-but-majority view – the majority might hate what your study shows, but if you're scientifically right, they can't scientifically prove you wrong.

It can help to think of the early days of psychiatry like the early days of explorers – there was so much mystery and uncharted territory! These famous and eccentric men and women (almost always men) could suddenly stumble across whole islands, even continents and desperately try to comprehend them, often accidentally finding something they weren't looking for, like Columbus finding America when looking for India.

Long before anyone was throwing the word autism around, autistics were still roaming the earth (or, more likely, staying in their rooms). There are plenty of historical accounts of very shy, eccentric obsessives who seemed able to remember everything about one area of expertise and had no close friends and so on and so forth. In the early days of psychiatry, they would throw enormous categories around, conflating autism with schizophrenia, psychopathy and who knows what else. During the first decades of the twentieth century, in the psychiatric establishment's struggle to come to grips with autism and classify it, autistic people could end up described as 'developmentally retarded', 'introverted personality types' or even 'idiot savants'.

Naturally, many of these diagnoses were only slapped onto people whose symptoms were severe enough to meet the attention of these psychiatrists and who were poor, or orphaned, or sectioned, or arrested, or similarly disadvantaged and discriminated against. If you were a rich, connected, educated white man and were able to 'function' at a high enough level you could get away with merely being an 'eccentric genius' like suspected autistics Mozart, Einstein, Isaac Newton or Henry Cavendish. These contrasting reactions from society illustrate the gulf between what has casually (never medically) been called 'high functioning' autism and 'low functioning' autism, a controversial description that uses academic ability and achievement to measure a person's 'functioning' and their worth or value. In reality, even these geniuses found it incredibly difficult to function in society and were considered socially utterly bizarre, but when people say 'high functioning' what they mean is 'We are happy to accept your difference *on the basis that you are an era-defining genius.*' It's almost like they're saying, OK, I will tolerate you, treat you nicely, treat you like a human being and take your needs seriously, but either I or society had better be getting something in return, something *big*, like *gravity*. The neurotypicals do not stop to ask themselves what amazing level of achievement *they* have reached to deserve to be treated with empathy.

In 1908 a psychiatrist called Eugen Bleuler coined the term 'autism'[24] and used it to describe a sort of severe withdrawal into yourself, introversion and self-admiration. The first person to define what we now consider to be autism was a female Ukrainian psychiatrist called Grunya Sukhareva.[25] She worked in a psychiatric hospital in Kyiv between 1917 and 1921 and in 1921 she founded a school for children with psychological issues in Moscow. Based on her work there, she published a paper in 1925 where she described 'schizoid personality disorder' and her description, taking into account the harsh nature of mental healthcare at the time, fits well

24   Kuhn R. (September 2004). 'Eugen Bleuler's concepts of psychopathology'. *History of Psychiatry*. 15 (59 Pt 3): 361–366.

25   Irina Manouilenko & Susanne Bejerot (2015). 'Sukhareva—Prior to Asperger and Kanner'. *Nordic Journal of Psychiatry*, 69:6, 1761 1764. DOI: 10.3109/08039488.2015. 1005022

even with modern diagnostic definitions like the DSM-5. She even uses the word 'autistic' within this definition, although not in the way we'd use it now. So, the word was around! But as described above, all these medical words change all the time, so you must always read the word in the context of the decade or even *the year* it was used and by whom.

During the 1930s a psychiatrist called Leo Kanner working in the United States ended up discovering and identifying autism in children as Kanner's syndrome[26] and, because the autism was obvious enough to be identified that early, ended up developing his diagnostic criteria on a form of autism that more often came with (or seemed to come with) intellectual impairment.[27] The autism would have to have been more obvious in order for it to show up so early; his investigations took place when his patients were so young, often babies, he wouldn't necessarily have been testing autistic people like me, who hid in plain sight.

At the same time, in Austria a psychiatrist called Hans Asperger was conducting similar research and he came to very similar, although not identical, conclusions to Kanner. Asperger, however, identified that a significant minority of his patients seemed to behave like little adults and displayed deep, obsessive interest in very specific topics which they could discuss at a higher level than expected. He nicknamed them his 'little professors'.[28] Looking back, it seems as though both

---

26   Robison, J. E. (2017). Kanner, Asperger, and Frankl: 'A third man at the genesis of the autism diagnosis'. *Autism, 21*(7), 862–871. https://DOI.org/10.1177/1362361316654283

27   *ibid.*

28   McPartland, J. C., Klin, A., Volkmar, F. R. & Felder, M. A. (2014). *Asperger syndrome: assessing and treating high-functioning autism spectrum disorders* (2nd ed.). New York: Guilford. p.5.

men were, while making errors and misunderstanding some things, describing different levels of the same thing: autism.

It is here we introduce the controversy, which comes in two portions so I hope you are hungry. The main course is about the man Hans Asperger, the dessert is about how we define 'functioning' and whether or not how clever you are is any of your doctor's business.

Hans Asperger was conducting his research in Austria during Nazi rule. He published his landmark paper describing autistic symptoms in 1944 and so it had little impact in the Anglophone world, which was otherwise preoccupied.[29] While Asperger was never a member of the Nazi Party, he was a member of several affiliated political organisations[30] – though it would have been difficult to advance one's career without joining at least one of these organisations, if not the party itself. He did sign his correspondence 'Heil Hitler'[31] but, again, it may have been unwise not to. This lack of Nazi Party membership is what ensured his continued academic career after the war and kept him away from controversy until recently.

Crucially, Asperger himself defended his reputation while he was alive, claiming that at one point he had to be saved from the Gestapo by his more-connected mentor, Franz Hamburger,[32] and that he had to join the army to escape Gestapo reprisals for refusing to cooperate with Nazi 'racial

29 Robison, J. E. (2017). Kanner, Asperger, and Frankl: 'A third man at the genesis of the autism diagnosis'. *Autism*, *21*(7), 862–871. https://DOI.org/10.1177/1362361316654283

30 Czech, H. (2018). Hans Asperger, 'National Socialism, and "race hygiene" in Nazi-era Vienna'. *Molecular Autism* 9, 29. https://DOI.org/10.1186/s13229-018-0208-6

31 *ibid.*

32 Feinstein A. (2010). *A History of Autism: Conversations with the Pioneers.* 1st ed. Chichester: Wiley-Blackwell.

hygiene' policies. This contributed to his later reputation as a man who did his best to resist, however passively, Nazi policy and to do his best for his disabled patients. It is only in the twenty-first century that more light has been shed on those early years of Asperger's career. Much of Asperger's good press has been contradicted or clarified by Herwig Czech and Edith Sheffer, who both published on the issue in 2018.[33] This newer research has yet to filter through the whole population, so be forgiving of anyone who is an Asperger fan based on older information when his story seemed much clearer-cut, more clearly a story of a smart, dedicated man doing his best in an incredibly difficult situation.

It appears that while Asperger was confident that the 'little professors' under his care could integrate into the Volk, or national community of Nazi Germany,[34] the other children in his care with more severe disabilities, or even just bedwetters or children of alcoholics, were sent away to a clinic in Vienna. There, they were experimented upon and often killed.[35] It is impossible to prove that Asperger specifically knew or intended this, however the shockingly high rate of mortality at these clinics was already a matter of public concern in Austria at the time,[36] with deaths from starvation, experimentation,

33 Czech, H. & Hans Asperger. (2018). 'National Socialism, and "race hygiene" in Nazi-era Vienna'. *Molecular Autism* 9, 29. https://DOI.org/10.1186/s13229-018-0208-6
Sheffer, E. (2018). *Asperger's Children: The Origins of Autism in Nazi Vienna.*

34 Asperger H. (1938). 'Das psychisch abnorme Kind. Wien Klin Wochenschr'. 49:1314–7.

35 Thomas, F. P., Beres, A. & Shevell, M. I. (2006). '"A Cold Wind Coming": Heinrich Gross and Child Euthanasia in Vienna'. *Journal of Child Neurology.* 21(4):342–348. DOI:10.1177/08830738060210040101

36 Czech, H. & Hans Asperger. (2018). 'National Socialism, and "race hygiene" in Nazi-era Vienna'. *Molecular Autism* 9, 29. https://DOI.org/10.1186/s13229-018-0208-6

torture or even lethal injection often categorised as deaths from 'pneumonia', a common method across the Reich to disguise the fate of the disabled, or induced using barbiturates over time.[37] Asperger did, however, seem to have defended some of his patients from forced sterilisation on the basis that it was uncalled for as they would be able to, with social help, 'occupy their place in the large organism of our people'.[38] These patients with a potential for social integration were worth saving and the rest were to be institutionalised or worse. This fits with the eugenicist, hyper-utilitarian ideas that were popular at the time even in democracies and, while it appears that Asperger was not 'full Nazi' in favour of sterilisation and sometimes didn't recommend it, he was not against it either. Indeed, he spoke up only when the individual seemed like they might be worth it to *Die Volk*. Not exactly the hero we would have wanted.

For many people, these biographical details alone would be enough to justify removing his name from anything. However, let's just say that if you start trying to cut the eugenicists out of scientific history you will end up with some very blunt scissors. Additionally, in certain fields, you will have trouble ignoring the contribution of scientists who were affiliated with or members of the Nazi Party at some point. Just ask the American and Soviet space programmes. It would be facile to claim that there was no scientific value in Asperger's texts, especially historically – his positive view of *some* autistic people, however minor, would take decades to be replicated

---

37 Czech H. (2014). 'Abusive medical practices on "euthanasia" victims in Austria during and after world war II'. In: Rubenfeld, S. & Benedict, S. (eds) 'Human subjects research after the Holocaust'. Cham, Heidelberg, New York *et al*. Springer; 2014. pp. 109–25.

38 Asperger H. (1938). 'Das Psychisch Abnorme Kind. Wien Klin Wochenschr'. 49:1314–7.

in the United States. The true debate over Asperger is a larger debate about affiliation, historical guilt and how we can ever truly know if someone worked with a deadly authoritarian government out of fear, love, practicality or all three. However, given that there are *so many* other psychiatrists who also described or 'discovered' autism at the same time as, or even earlier than, Hans Asperger, it does seem odd to demand that we keep the name of the guy who used to sign his letters 'Heil Hitler'. It's like I always say, if you can avoid an affiliation with the Nazi Party, you should.[39]

In fact, the term 'Asperger's syndrome' was never officially used during Hans Asperger's lifetime. His work was little translated, especially the early pre- and mid-war research. It was the English psychiatrist Lorna Wing who, in 1981, first suggested 'Asperger's syndrome' to describe 'children and adults who have autistic features, but who talk grammatically and who are not socially aloof'.[40] Lorna Wing explained that Asperger's syndrome's features could be found to varying degrees in the whole population, but that the diagnosis of Asperger's could explain cases where the difference was so marked that it couldn't just be explained by variation. In other words, we all love some alone time with a good book, but what about this guy who *needs* alone time with a *lot* of very *specific* books for way more hours a week?

Then, in the 1990s, the ICD-10 and the DSM-4 both recognised Asperger's syndrome as an official condition that was *distinct* from but *related to* autistic disorder or childhood autism. One of

39 Not just good advice for the medical profession – good advice for all of us!

40 Wing L. (1981). 'Asperger's syndrome: a clinical account'. *Psychol Med.* Feb; 11(1):115-29. DOI: 10.1017/s0033291700053332. PMID: 7208735.

the main differences was that people with Asperger's syndrome, as opposed to autism, experienced no difficulty or delay with the development of speech or language and in fact may display aspects of early or advanced development in these areas. (For example, when I was two years old a family friend asked me what I thought of my newborn sister. I replied that 'she disturbs my mind'. Chilling. Like dialogue from *The Omen*.) Basically, the layman's perspective at the time was, as far as I remember, that Asperger's was 'high functioning' and autism wasn't.

By 2013, several convincing scientific arguments had been made that Asperger's syndrome was simply not clearly distinct enough from autism. Autism was so clearly a condition with an enormous spectrum of possible effects and symptoms that it didn't make scientific sense to slice a piece of it off and call it Asperger's. Indeed, studies proved that a distinct diagnosis of Asperger's vs autism was not possible across a range of physicians.[41] It would be a bit like calling Covid-19 a different name if you didn't get the cough, although that is a crude analogy that I am sure is inappropriate and I look forward to being told off online. On this basis, in 2013 the DSM-5 took Asperger's, autistic disorder, along with the other conditions CDD and PDD-NOS, and smooshed them into the broader concept of 'Autism Spectrum Disorder'. It also added the support levels 1, 2 and 3. This change also had the bonus

---

41 Lord, C., Petkova, E., Hus, V., Gan, W., Lu, F., Martin, D. M., Ousley, O., Guy, L., Bernier, R., Gerdts, J., Algermissen, M., Whitaker, A., Sutcliffe, J. S., Warren, Z., Klin, A., Saulnier, C., Hanson, E., Hundley, R., Piggot, J., Fombonne, E., Steiman, M., Miles, J., Kanne, S. M., Goin-Kochel, R. P., Peters, S. U., Cook, E. H., Guter, S., Tjernagel, J., Green-Snyder, L. A., Bishop, S., Esler, A., Gotham, K., Luyster, R., Miller, F., Olson, J., Richler, J. & Risi, S. 'A multisite study of the clinical diagnosis of different autism spectrum disorders'. *Arch Gen Psychiatry*. Mar; 69(3):306–13. DOI: 10.1001/archgenpsychiatry.2011.148. Epub 2011 Nov 7. PMID: 22065253; PMCID: PMC3626112.

of ending or avoiding the unscientific (but historical, moral, philosophical, ethical) debate over the acceptability of the name of Hans Asperger. Those diagnosed with Asperger's during that earlier period still 'have' it but are able to sort of 'convert' it to ASD-1, should they wish. Many of these people are against renaming the condition as they feel Asperger's syndrome describes them better, or they feel the name is a part of their identity and resent a faceless medical organisation taking that away from them. That's fair enough. The ICD-11 from 2022 is a little more granular in the sense that it has several subdivisions of autism. It's like a waiter asking: 'Autism with or without intellectual development, sir? I see, and will that be with mild or no language impairment? Impaired language? Or complete or almost complete functional language?' My order is autism without disorder of intellectual development and with complete functional language, otherwise known as 6A02.5 – it's delicious, try it with lemon, pair it with a Chablis etc. Subdivisions aside, essentially it's all autism from now on.

Changing the names does also make it harder to make yourself understood to the general public. The years from 1990 to 2013 were a boom time for public awareness about autism and Asperger's. If Asperger's was a brand, it was achieving some incredible market penetration. It's all very well discussing your marvellous neurodivergence if you're like me, hanging out with people who work in the arts in some hipster basement, but one of the advantages of throwing the term Asperger's around for over two decades is that it was far easier to explain yourself to the old fella in the pub. I didn't even know they changed it in 2012 until 2022.

This is one of the disadvantages of losing it as a term –

it undoes a great deal of public awareness that we must now rebuild from the ground up. To this day I often find it easier to say Asperger's instead of autism, or maybe I'll say autism and follow it up with Asperger's, because in that moment I am (in my head) saying to the person, 'I have autism, but not the most difficult kind' – I wouldn't want to seem like I was claiming any severe difficulties that I do not face. However, this can too easily slip into, 'I have autism, but not the *bad* kind, not the kind you're *afraid of*, or that *I'm afraid of*, if I'm really honest. I'm not *stupid*, I swear! I'm actually a huge nerd! Is that better?' Oh God! It feels somehow safer to reassure whoever you are speaking to that you aren't as disabled as they might fear and that they don't need to feel bad for you, but it can enhance prejudice, not diminish it.

Functioning

This brings us to the 'functioning' controversy, as discussed earlier. Ability to function and lack of intellectual impairment was one of the main arguments behind keeping Asperger's separate. However, part of why they switched to an umbrella term of autism with added support levels was because of how intellectually or philosophically inconsistent the idea of 'functioning' had become. Let's take Isaac Newton as an example of someone who almost certainly had what was called Asperger's syndrome.[42] He would definitely be called 'high functioning' by the average person, what with the whole 'revolutionising humanity's understanding of science'

42   James I. 'Singular scientists'. *J R Soc Med.* 2003 Jan; 96(1):36-9. DOI: 10.1177/014107680309600112. PMID: 12519805; PMCID: PMC539373.

thing. However, how high functioning was he? As a *person*? From what we know, he hardly ever spoke, he never married and may have died a virgin. He had no friends as a boy and frequently fell out with the few adult friends he later had; he became so obsessed with his work that he often forgot to eat or drink; he was renowned at Cambridge for being slovenly dressed on the rare occasions he dined with others; and if no one showed up to his lectures, he'd deliver them to an empty room. At the age of fifty, he had an enormous breakdown after long periods of depression and paranoia.[43] Is this a well-functioning man in any area of his life outside academia? And this is his level of functioning *with* access to servants! Or is this, more accurately and using the most modern diagnosis we have, an autistic man without impaired intellectual development? A man with many of the same needs as an intellectually impaired autistic man but with better ability to express and repress them, and a (morally) completely unrelated ability in mathematics and science? The idea here is that if a change in your routine makes you freak out, then that's that; it is medically irrelevant if that is a change in your lecturing schedule as a professor or a change in your schedule as a gravedigger. Your needs are your needs, it does not matter if you are able to function intellectually at a very high level or if you have managed to earn lots of money.[44]

This idea is pushed even further by people online, with

43 Wakely, Elizabeth & Carson, Jerome (2011). 'Historical recovery heroes – Isaac Newton'. *Mental Health and Social Inclusion*. 15. 122-128. 10.1108/20428301111165708.

44 The super-genius part only becomes medically relevant when it reaches the standards of savantism – Newton may have been a savant, it's hard to tell. However, for modern purposes, savantism has a high bar and is rare. It's far more statistically likely that you're just dealing with a highly intelligent person who *happens* to have autism.

some describing it as morally wrong, even a legacy of Nazi eugenics, to ever point out any intellectual distinctions within disabilities or conditions like autism. That any attempt to do so is merely another way of weeding out the 'good' disabled people from the 'bad' disabled people, where 'good' means 'useful to me or society in my opinion'. I would argue that it *can* be wrong, but we will always need to distinguish between *severity of need*. It is ridiculous to pretend that I need the same level of support in life as someone who is non-verbal, someone who has severe panic attacks or violent public meltdowns. It's the difference between utopian or abstract, philosophical thinking and pragmatic thinking. I don't think there will ever be a way to stop people from linking their idea of 'functioning' with someone's worth, unfortunately, and there are vital, good-hearted reasons to differentiate between who needs more or less of your help.

Remember when I mentioned above how 'idiot' was once a medical term? The reason it is now an insult is down to something called the 'euphemism treadmill'. Words begin their life as medical terminology (idiot, spastic, retarded) and, as the knowledge filters from academia down to the public, they become insults. It doesn't seem like we'll ever be able to pick a word and settle on it for these things – the meaning changes too much and medical terminology needs a little mystery to jolt people into taking it seriously. Kids are already bullying each other online using the word autism, so a new word is travelling down the treadmill as you read this. Who knows what it will be next! Shouting 'intellectually impaired' takes too long – by the time you're done they're round the corner – whereas 'idiot', 'spastic', 'retard' are all plosive, snappy little words that are as throwable as cricket balls. Also, the word 'neurodivergent' is inherently the sort of language a nerd would use and as a result the bully would have to instantly turn the bullying upon themselves lest they be accused of hypocrisy, the ultimate sin in the bullying community. That being said, I think the DSM's support levels of 1, 2 and 3 do a fairly good job of making these distinctions without getting too eerily obsessed with anyone's GCSE results or the shape of their skull.

Another issue with letting people label you as high or low functioning is the fact that they could simply be wrong. After all, there are plenty of incompetent or uncaring medical or educational workers out there, and even when they are kind and trying their best, they can get the wrong end of the stick. Someone labelled 'low functioning' can grow up to become 'high functioning' – for example, the speaker and academic Dr Temple Grandin, who was diagnosed as brain-damaged and her parents told to institutionalise her and get on with their lives. The fact that she started out as 'low functioning' to the point of seeming brain damaged but ended up a famous speaker and academic led to an erroneous view that people can 'grow out of their autism'; it's easier to claim that than admitting our metrics for measuring and predicting functioning are garbage.

When I was a child, I had one teacher tell my parents that I should be checked for deafness and a primary school teacher claimed that, at the age of nine, I had completely failed literacy, as well as several other key progress markers. In truth, I simply ignored or didn't bother fully filling in any tests that were handed out. Why should I? They were boring and no one ever told me what they were for. My kind and patient mother had to sit me down, aged ten, and explain the entire purpose and concept of tests to me, how to answer them and why I should bother. After her intervention, it was success all the way. In some ways it is too risky to let some outsider define the potential of your child – after all, who died and made them king of functioning?

There is a darker side to emphasising 'high functioning' autistic people. We are already seeing an argument from autistic people with high support needs complaining that autistic people labelled 'high functioning' are used against them as examples that prove their extra needs are exaggerated or non-existent. Some parents describe how the prevailing narrative of autism as a superpower, or, tragically, the examples of successful autistic people, are creating a negative impact on the extra support that their children need, if for example they have additional learning difficulties, cerebral palsy or do not use speech as their main method of communication.[45] As a result, we do still need differentiation of some kind, so that the public and, by extension, the government, doesn't use 'high functioning low support' autistic people like me as a stick to beat all the others with. Regardless, in ten years, twenty years, all the terminology will change again. I suppose the entire message of this chapter is: don't get too comfortable.

---

45 Buchan, Dr L. (2024). Voice note to author, 9 January.

CHAPTER 3

Have You Ever Felt Like a Social Fraud?

Autism inherently comes with social difficulties. As you grow up and realise that you are different to others, not only in a deep way but also in a way that people don't seem to like, you will either consciously or unconsciously learn to 'mask' your autism to hide it from wider society. This could be in order to socialise more successfully, avoid bullying, progress in school or your career, or avoid punishments and misunderstandings. Basically, 'masking' is hiding things about yourself to soften the negative impact of expressing your autistic self.

I remember the first time I masked. I was at primary school, sitting in class and learning some important child maths. In one question, various children were trying to see who had the most apples, as children do. These children were measuring their various apple-hoard sizes via a pie chart and it was down to muggins here to tell them who had the most apples in various combos. So far so normal. The only problem was that the worksheet had been photocopied using whatever diesel-powered Soviet photocopier they had access to and you couldn't quite discern the sections in the image. Very dark, very blobby. This is around the year 2000 we're talking, after all: overhead projectors, no mobile phones for anyone but fancy businessmen, Pokémon cards being banned from school for driving children insane with jealousy and envy.

I had raised my hand and asked the teacher to clarify which image was which – a simple query, but it had all gone terribly wrong. Now, the teacher was leaning over me and explaining the whole exercise to me. I had asked a precise question about a minor element of the task and, instead of receiving a quick answer to that exact question, my query was a chance to have the entire task laboriously explained to me again. In hindsight, the teacher was kindly making sure I understood everything, assuming that I was more like a neurotypical child who would have been afraid or self-conscious about not understanding a task and so would downplay it by only asking about one bit of the task. Nope. I was very much just hoping for a quick response to my very specific question so that I, robo-boy, could return to my work.

As the teacher explained the entire thing to me all over again, I listened with a neutral facial expression. Slowly, we traipsed through the concept of pie charts, the idea of segments, the word ratio was thrown around and, when my expression remained neutral, the word ratio was heavily explained. Part of the way through they identified the segments of the pie chart – so *that* dark blob represented Siobhan's apples! Aha! My question was finally answered! However, it was not over. I had to keep listening. When I was a child the feeling of boredom was agony to me; if I could have, I would have already been dousing myself with petrol. However, I was also raised to be scrupulously polite, a frightening little butler, so I knew I couldn't interrupt the teacher – what could be ruder? So, I sat and took my medicine. When they had finished, they asked me if I understood. I replied, with my little neutral face:

'Yes.'

They looked at me for a few seconds, sighed in irritation and immediately explained the entire thing to me again from the beginning.

I was confused and irritated – why the fuck was this happening again? I had said yes! Then I realised that I had clearly not done something crucial with my voice and face. My voice and my face had failed me utterly: I seemed like I did not understand at all. Worst of all, the teacher was clearly indirectly calling me a liar. I was sitting here, seeming like a *stupid liar*, the very worst kind of liar.

The solution was clear: I would have to perform a one-man play entitled: 'The boy who slowly came to understand the task'. As the teacher began again, I nodded thoughtfully through the basics. Nod, nod, nod, yes, this part I understand, very good. Then, when the teacher came to discuss the segments of the pie chart, identifying each of them in turn, I furrowed my brow a little, frowning, tilted my head as if listening harder. As they identified each segment I changed this expression to a slow-dawning smile of comprehension and began nodding again, maybe throwing in an 'OK' or 'right' here and there. Then, the big final question: 'Do you understand now?'

'Yup, yeah, for sure,'[46] I said, nodding and smiling. Success! The teacher said 'Good' and left me alone, free to continue with my work and relieved of the pain of awkward social pretence.

I had learned a valuable lesson, even if subconsciously: your words are not enough, your face is wrong. It took me years to consciously realise that I wasn't doing enough with my face and that interactions like this gave people the idea that I was stupid, and in fairness I did often ask childishly direct questions about obvious things with a blank face, like an idiot would. I could sense that people found something odd about my vibe and that I was constantly misunderstood but could never figure out what it was, or why, or how to fix it. I just knew I needed to nod and smile.

Stimming

Physical masking isn't just about doing extra facial expressions for non-autistics' sake. It is also about suppressing physical things that you would actively like to do, such as 'stimming'.

Stimming is self-stimulating behaviour that is unconventional, intense or repetitive and it can take many forms. The more commonly recognised forms are hand-flapping, knee-jigging, finger-flicking. It can also involve objects like flicking a rubber band, twirling a piece of string or repeatedly touching a particular texture. When I wear a hoodie, I enjoy

---

46 For some reason saying a simple, plain 'yes' makes people see you as a complete bullshitter. If you repeatedly say 'yes' but using slang or abbreviated variations of the word you come across as much more possessed and comprehending for some reason. I have noticed posher people in the UK doing this, saying, 'Yah, no, yah, absolutely, for sure, of course, yah' instead of just 'yes'. There may be a link between shallow plausibility and class, who's to say?

fiddling with the little end bits of the drawstrings and rubbing them between thumb and forefinger. I recommend growing a moustache if you enjoy stimming as it is definitely satisfying to stroke, although you will look evil.

Stimming might just sound like a fancy word for fidgeting but they differ in some key ways. Fidgeting is often an attempt to remedy a physical discomfort, like a hard chair, whereas stimming is done in response to psychological stimuli. People might stim in response to an overwhelming environment, sensory overload or extreme emotion. I find that the hoodie string or moustache stroking helps me concentrate and focus, or if I am in a very stressful situation, it calms me down and allows me to centre myself. Put me on a noisy, overheated train where people are loudly eating smelly food and bumping into me and I imagine I'll stroke my moustache right off my face. There are some forms of stimming that are self-injurious, such as scratching or hitting yourself, and in these cases you'll have to learn to avoid or minimise situations that trigger these. It's not always negative, though. Stimming is also something that might be done for pleasure or to express extreme joy. If I am relaxing watching a film I'll generally fiddle with some bit of string or blanket, and some autistic people may flap their hands, jump or spin as part of being excited.

You can also stim through echolalia, which is repeating words, phrases or sounds to yourself. I do this A LOT around the flat, especially with unusual phrases or accents. I live near a railway and my old flatmate and I used to compulsively imitate the train horn that would sound as trains passed on the nearby track, just wandering around the kitchen, watching television, quietly honking to ourselves in perfect unison whenever we heard the train. Sometimes even mid-conversation: 'Hey, was there a package delivered this – heehonk – morning?'

Suffice to say, if you are a teenager and you go around honking to yourself and flapping your hands, you're going to get your fucking head kicked in. Time to mask! OK, maybe not as bad as that, but you're going to be socially excluded until you learn to ruthlessly suppress your urge to stim.

This might just sound like socialisation to you if you are non-autistic. It might sound reasonable, like teaching children not to rock on their chairs. However, there is a safety aspect to supressing stimming that is dangerous to the autistic person or others, especially in children, or if the behaviour could impact a person's opportunities or ability to learn. There's an aspect of adjustment to society that is unavoidable, it's true, but outside of these explicitly negative examples suppressing stimming is not just socialisation. You are taking autistic people aside and forcing them to choose between expressing themselves and loneliness or bullying. Stimming is instinctive and either pleasurable or a coping mechanism or both, like laughter. If enough people found your laughter irritating or weird, would you be able to stop yourself from ever laughing again unless you were in private? Would you want to?

Look at this!

A form of masking that is not physical is learning to repress your enthusiasm for things, especially your potentially unusual 'special interests'. As I was an undiagnosed child, I had no idea that autistic people generally had intense special interests that they loved to discuss that MIGHT be socially burdensome for others. All I knew was that I was nine years old and the 1950s radio comedy show *The Goon Show*, starring Spike Milligan, Peter Sellers and Harry Secombe, was the greatest piece of art produced in human history. The pyramids themselves could not compare. None of my other primary school-age friends seemed to agree, however, no matter how many small bursts of Goons I played them from the cassettes I borrowed from the library.[47]

Their lack of interest certainly taught me that, in theory, people did not enjoy hearing about my interests, but I am afraid I applied that lesson exclusively to *The Goon Show*. I spent many of my teenage years gamely trying to interest my fellow tweens in the ongoing Iraq War, George W. Bush's relationship with evangelical American right, the niche web-based flash cartoon series *Homestar Runner*, and the weaponry of the Second World War, but to no avail. They insisted on focusing on the endless Manchester United vs Liverpool debate (being a recent immigrant from South Africa, I had little idea where these places even were), watching MTV and coveting Von Dutch caps. I was confounded: who would want to watch Britney Spears dicking about when they could be listening to the greatest British radio comedy of the 1950s?

I couldn't understand it – these things were clearly the greatest and most interesting possible things going on, the most important, the funniest things, weren't they? I can honestly say that, with a few nerdy exceptions, people *really fucking hated* hearing about this stuff. Well-meaning neurotypicals

---

47 What an OLD SENTENCE. How OLD! I am about to turn thirty-two at time of writing and this sentence is the kind of thing you should hear being mumbled from deep within an armchair.

were always dishing out advice on making friends like 'Talk about your interests!', unaware that this advice would unleash a dreadful gibbering tide of statistics and trivia upon the poor, unsuspecting classmates, relatives and teachers of one Pierre Novellie. Over time this became less of a problem: I managed to rein it in, at least a bit,[48] by absorbing the following painful lesson: in general, you must assume no one agrees with you about this stuff being worthwhile. Or, more bluntly: all the things you think are interesting are boring, all the things you think are boring are interesting. It was a very shaming and sobering thing to absorb and it is one of the reasons I apologise for my interests to this very day, and why I am disproportionately delighted when I meet someone who shares them. It also didn't hurt that, as we got older, my classmates became more aware of, say, politics or comedy or history, thus giving these little nuggets of trivia I dispensed some sort of value.

I always felt as though there was something 'off' about me – I had no idea what it was, I just knew that the way people reacted to me heavily suggested that I was not what they were expecting. In the worst-case scenarios, I would be humiliated or embarrassed by the sheer extent to which I had got something 'wrong', socially.

That sense of being perceived as wrong, other or weird is a large part of the motivation for creating a mask, whether you know you are autistic or not. As you grow up you are aware that there is a correlation between being yourself or saying

48 There may be people reading this who I have bored half to death with a rambling explanation of some niche phenomenon and these people may scoff and say, 'Reined it in? The man's reined in nothing!' To you I say: 'You do not know how lucky you are, and how much more boring and strange it could have been.'

what you really think and mockery, rejection or confusion. It is terrible to admit to your peers that you do not understand the joke, or why someone would do something, or what is supposed to be fun about something you hate. The fear of being psychologically nude in front of one's peers is crippling for adults, never mind teenagers.

As a teenager you will be punished for sharing things that delight you if they don't fit with the crowd and, with autism, they almost by definition won't. The lesson is clear: the thing that makes you feel alive, that gives you a profound sense of delight and illumination and meaning, is probably really boring to everyone else. Over time, you might learn to automatically repress that little spark you feel when you want to share something great with the people around you. It's a tough thing to unlearn when you grow up. When you are an adult, you can create a social web of people that delight in the same things you do, and I am incredibly lucky to have done so.

Why can't I get along with people?

When I was a young teenager I came to the realisation that, whatever I was doing socially, it was not working for me. The party or social invitations that had gone my way for years had stopped almost immediately around age twelve, as if by mass silent agreement, and occasions where I socialised with anyone outside of school shrunk to zero. Unless everybody was just too busy managing their new crop of pubes, it was clear there was a problem – I just had no idea what it was. My Bebo was dead! My MSN Messenger silent, regardless of how many times I appeared offline and then online again to get attention. After a year or two of baffled isolation I decided to use the one asset I had for sure – academic intelligence – to solve the problem. I was going to observe, analyse and imitate the successful social habits of people in my year.[49] You know, like a creepy scientist or an alien dressed as a child. (It goes without saying that I learned to speak the language of 'teenage boy in the British Isles in the noughties', so if you don't fully relate to the dynamics I outline then that is probably why – apologies if you never did the finger 'OK' sign punch game from *Malcolm in the Middle*, rubbed a magnet on someone's iPod Shuffle to destroy it or constantly quoted bloody *Anchorman*.)

A lot of my weirdness was excused or covered by the fact that I was an immigrant – I moved from South Africa to the Isle of Man when I was about seven years old. Being South African explained to many British people that it was to be expected that I was more blunt, direct and happy to follow rules than they were. One of the British social subjects I was failing terribly in was banter. Strange, given that I am now a professional stand-up comedian, but true. I had been raised to be 'nice' and 'polite', which, when it comes to teenage banter and male bonding, is about as much use as a corpse in goal. Years of good parenting and vague 'do unto others' demi-Christian rhetoric had withered my banter muscles away to nothing and, frankly, the concept didn't make any sense to me. Why would I be rude to my friends? Especially when it

---

49 For years I thought this was just a marvellously clever strategy that I was enterprising enough to invent. You can imagine how my blood ran cold to discover that this was the autistic equivalent of learning to drive – every bloody medical resource, biography, Reddit post about autism or masking or Asperger's describes this exact process.

came to their obvious failings! Surely we should be rude to our enemies and nice to our friends?

What I didn't understand is that there is an intimacy to rudeness – you are testing a boundary and seeing if the other person is so confident in themselves and in your affection for them that they can discount and even enjoy this rudeness. You and your friend are trading insecurities, trusting each other not to be cruel, and demonstrating confidence in yourselves and your friendship at the same time.

Conversely, politeness is actually reserved for strangers and represents a wall between you and the other person: I am being polite to you up until I decide if it is safe to be myself. It says to the other person, 'We are not close, not in my opinion. I will not be vulnerable to you. Good day, sir.' In British society, politeness is generally reserved for your worst enemies, so my weird manners had no place in this environment. I was wandering around school like Anthony Hopkins in *Remains of the Day* and my classmates were re-creating *Lord of the Flies*.

Over time, I realised that my problem was that I had always taken banter or taunts at face value and, frankly, couldn't tell the difference between someone teasing me and someone trying to insult me. My problem had always been how seriously I took the jokes – I was not a laugh. Someone would mock my accent or the way I did something and I would kick off, lash out. It's still not a distinction I can always make, as some otherwise good-natured hecklers have discovered to their cost.[50] I watched carefully as various boys in my year

---

50 An apology to the group of Geordie men in a Leicester Square comedy club some time in 2015 who banterously referred to me as a 'massive fookin' ginger bastard'. In hindsight that was at least 60 per cent banter and I mostly regret my remarks about your appearances and genetic closeness with your relatives.

traded jibes with each other that would have made me furious, trying to figure out where the line was between banter and asking for a smack.

There were all sorts of techniques: a simple come-back, the old switcheroo where, for example, if someone said your hair was terrible, you could just imply that taking care of your hair was in some way the behaviour of a paedophile. If your critic had an unusual voice, a simple impression would quickly neutralise their comment, regardless of how accurate it was. It was like trying to learn martial arts by watching YouTube videos but, slowly, progress was made.

My favourite, for its grace and humility, was the eager embrace of the insult followed by a topper. My friend Stephen was the master of this, acknowledging eagerly that not only did he have sex with his mother but that he was particularly skilled at it, for example. Or, in another memorable scenario when someone accused him of losing his hair, he gleefully informed them about his apparently tiny penis. This had the dual effect of neutralising the insult, making people laugh and, with any luck, potentially revolting the original accuser. In teenage-boy-land, whoever was grossed out was often the loser of the bout. For someone with my level of sensitivity to insult, the idea of embracing, of leaning into it, was a revelation that verged on the spiritual. The strength it took!

The other baffling thing to me was how these people could stamp all over each other's insecurities in rugby boots and, the next day, be friends again! Sometimes even better friends. Because I was more sensitive to insult, I simply couldn't tell how these guys were deciding between laughing it off or kicking off, there didn't seem to be a pattern at all.

HAVE YOU EVER FELT LIKE A SOCIAL FRAUD?

This needed fixing, because my own radar was so fucked that it held me back from ever joking around with someone and, in British social culture, that is absolutely unforgiveable. The reason I always held back was that, when I had tried to banter in the past, I had completely misjudged the level of force. A classmate would say something witty like 'nice tie, tie boy' and I would say something genuinely horrific about their appearance. Failure! Someone had lightly elbowed me in the ribs, metaphorically, and I had wheeled around and headbutted their nose into their face. This guy is not a laugh. Equally, every now and then someone said something to start a fight, some truly dark insult, and I would chortle and wave like a Royal on a balcony. It is hard to say which of the two responses that people found more unsettling.

I also noted how the people who got teased the most to their face were either socially successful or complete dickheads seen as far beyond redemption. It was interesting to see how negatively the social group reacted when someone teased an innocent, socially unsuccessful person – groans of disgust or eye rolls! The idea seemed to be that someone rich in social currency could afford to spend a little on being mocked and mocking someone lacking in social currency was the equivalent of mugging a homeless person, taking candy from a baby. Obviously, there were exceptions: high levels of cruelty would be justified by sheer level of wit and there was no discounting the base, animalistic mischief of the teenager as a motivating factor. Also, if people felt able to make fun of you, to take away from your social currency, it probably meant that they felt you could afford it. It was a compliment of sorts. The most devastating thing of all would be to be seen as such an easy target, such an object of pity and despair, that you *couldn't even be made fun of.* This meant that, if someone ribbed me, it meant I was succeeding – I could change my entire attitude based on this evidence. When it came down to it, it was all about learning the rules and I could certainly do that.

Did Robo-Boy succeed?

I know that to many readers much of what I have written above will seem like someone carefully writing out an explanation of how to go for a shit. However, this is my point: I had to learn all of this the same way that I learned French. It was not a natural response or driven by instinct. The reason it seems artificial is that I had to learn it in an artificial way. In fact, having a second language is the best way for me to think about it.[51] Imagine that you were born in England but you speak fluent French. You live and work in France but still think in English and speak English at home. So, I can get my work done and exist in a French-speaking society – in fact, I am so good at speaking French that I don't even seem English anymore! People are very surprised to discover that I am English and not a native speaker. However, it is exhausting. If I am tired or drunk, I will forget vital vocabulary or get things confused. It will never be as easy or as comfortable as just speaking English.

So there I was, between the ages of twelve and sixteen, learning my second language. Given how incredibly autistic

---

51 This is a shame because I am, like a good comedian, always looking for relatable examples and so few people in the UK speak a second language. I feel there is a risk I am saying something that just makes people more confused like 'masking my autism is like doing three backflips' or 'it's like killing a crow with your hands'.

that is, you are right to wonder how I evaded diagnosis at this stage. Well, firstly, this entire process took place in secret, entirely in my own head. I might've discussed elements of it with my parents but mainly it was a secret project divided between field experiments at school and social behaviour resources online. Many of the resources were self-help, self-help adjacent or academic. Some of them were, in hindsight, depressing blogs written by bitter people which luckily I managed not to take as gospel. This was around 2004–2007, remember – none of the current discourse around neurodivergence existed in popular culture.

One of the more wholesome resources was provided to me by my concerned parents, who were well aware that their son was a social flop. It was a sort of self-help book for teens where, in the introduction, the man writing it admits that as a student he was a great athlete but not much of a student. As an asthmatic hyper-nerd, this was already enough for me to launch the book, wheezing, into the recycling, but I was desperate and so kept reading. The first chapter was all about a teenage boy who, when he was feeling miserable and angry, went around expressing anger and inflicting it on his friends. *Expressing* misery and anger?! Friends?! Suffice to say, the book was abandoned.

Because this experiment was done in the privacy of my own mind, the sheer weirdness of what I was up to never came to the attention of the relevant diagnostic authorities. After all, I was a huge nerd and doing well academically, so what was the problem? Nerds are always odd. In terms of this being noticed by family, we were all a little weird anyway and, as immigrants from South Africa to the Isle of Man, there was a great deal of social behaviour in our new homeland that we all found utterly baffling. If my parents could be confused, why wouldn't I be?

What I can tell you is that it worked like a dream. I worked hard, probably harder than for many of my exams. The experiment was a success. I made new friends, began to be invited to parties and even won a student election. The transformation was dramatic, but it was aided by a few key factors that would have made my life easier anyway. As we got older and eventually entered sixth form, academic results became more relevant. Witty remarks began to be valued above the blunt, sledgehammer banter of the mid-teens. Alcohol became a consistent presence at parties, allowing everyone to relax their inhibitions and become less self-conscious, myself included. I do wonder how much of this transformation was actually down to my efforts and how much was down to everyone simply growing up – then I remember how I once tried to use a Shakespearian insult in conversation and I give myself some credit for the transformation.

I began to amass a combination of the different banter scripts in my mind and formed a sort of armoury of wit. I didn't always get it right but, over time, I got close *enough* to be accepted. It was a revelation to me how much conversation followed a sort of simple script or algorithm – it's one of the reasons that small-talk makes me want to push pencils into my eyes, because it's almost always the same.[52] I slowly

---

52 This desire for novelty has resulted in me being friends, in good ways and bad ways, with some incredibly odd, rude, funny or eccentric people over the years. It has been difficult learning that sometimes, when someone flouts a social norm, it is an indicator that there might be something badly wrong, and not that they are 'a laugh, and probably have some great stories'.

gained the confidence to try making jokes out loud or say the things I thought, be outspoken – I had always thought I was funny in my head but I had never said anything for fear of rejection. In my excitement, I am certain that a fair few of the funny thoughts I released into the world were as cruel as the sentiments thrown my way years earlier, but I justified this to myself as the price of doing business. After all, wasn't it just the way things worked and now I was a part of it? Sure, I felt like I was much less polite now, much less nice, but where had that ever got me? It was time to pop the collar of my polo shirt and take some top-down selfies!

The effect was dramatic enough that I remember one day in sixth form where someone was trying to reminisce with me about the various crazy parties we had attended over the years at the house of a boy we will call Smith. Smith had created a party nirvana weekend after weekend – an Eden of Smirnoff Ice, Blue WKDs or even, for the ambitious underage drinker, beer. He achieved what every noughties teen dreamed of: to re-create the completely unreasonable parties from *Skins*. The trouble was that Smith detested me, so I had never attended any of these incredible parties. In fact, he had an issue with me to the extent that he had snatched my GCSE results out of my hands on results day and asked, 'How did a retard like you get results like that?' – quick as a flash, I wittily shrugged and went 'Buh'. That showed him. Anyway, I told this person I had never been at these parties and they refused to believe it. They were certain I had been there and even went on Facebook to browse the various low-quality digital camera photos of the parties to try and find me in the background. I was quite disturbed to find that people were able to essentially rewrite their memories of events to accommodate a new reality rather than just admit that for years they had considered me a huge dork. As you get older, though, you realise that we all rewrite the past to fit the present to some extent, but I had learned another lesson: people's perceptions of you could be completely upside-down compared to yours and you might never even realise. And if people want someone to fit into their world, they will just make it happen in their own minds, regardless of the contradictions. Terrifying![53]

So, masking is about both hiding things that come naturally to you (intense interests, stimming) as well as engaging in additional behaviour that you wouldn't have otherwise (more facial expressions, small talk).

I would like to say here that I acknowledge that everyone suppresses or expresses themselves under the heavy yoke of peer pressure. We are all punched into shape by life's massive fists. However, the difference here is that autistics, especially undiagnosed ones, are forced into rejecting the very basis of how their mind works, to reject and ignore the way they perceive the world in exchange for acceptance. If you are undiagnosed, as I was, you see these differences in thought as a sign of some kind of fundamental stupidity, selfishness or moral flaw in yourself. The lesson you take from it is that your truest self is the least acceptable self, so you conceal it as best you can. It also means that when you succeed socially, when people like the masked version of

---

53   Score one for social anxiety! This revelation did not make me more confident; it made me lose faith in the idea of anyone having any solid perception of anyone else, so I immediately downgraded anything anyone said about anyone else to 'Maybe!', including myself. Academically thorough but emotionally exhausting, as I'm sure my former partners would say.

you, you feel like a fraud. They don't really like you, they like this creature you have built, and you feel a mild contempt: for them for being easily tricked, for yourself for needing tricks to be liked. It goes without saying that this doesn't make adult relationships easy and it can create all sorts of issues with regard to self-esteem. Generic teenage shame is often banished with rhetoric like 'Don't worry, everyone feels that way sometimes!' which, when it comes to autism, is not true. 'Don't worry, between 1 and maybe 5 per cent of people can feel this way sometimes!' doesn't have quite the same reassuring effect. Autistic masking is a lifelong practice and survival strategy that is mostly forced on us and uses up precious time and energy, as well as eroding your sense of self.

De-masking

Once people are diagnosed, they tend to go through a period of 'de-masking', which is probably more pronounced the older the person is, given that age will correlate with amount and depth of masking. This is because your diagnosis allows or forces you to question a lot of behaviours that have built up over your lifetime. If you are particularly heavily masked for decades and from a traditional background, you might have lived your entire life according to a set of assumptions without ever really figuring out what *you* wanted. There are some heart-breaking and dramatic accounts of people de-masking when middle-aged or older when they realise that they now feel they have been living a lie and suddenly move houses, change careers, even end marriages. Depending on the level of masking and the context, de-masking can be a beautiful pleasure or extremely risky.

No one is ever able to completely de-mask, of course. We are not lovers to our colleagues or collegiate with our lovers. However, it is important to sit and reflect on the extent to which you might be masking and inadvertently living for others far more than yourself. The pressures of your childhood or teenage years no longer apply! Who knows how much truer to yourself you could be. It might be difficult to de-mask if you are, like me, a heavily masked autistic who has been handsomely rewarded for masking for decades. You associate hiding your autism and difficulties caused by your autism with acceptance, success, friendship, social and professional advancement, even love. It's going to be intimidating and feel extremely risky to remove the mask that you credit with getting you where you are today. It feels logical to presume that if you lose the mask you lose what the mask has gained you, but that's not necessarily true. Besides, now that you know you have a mask it forces you to be self-aware about when you can be bothered to mask and forces you to reassess the value of masked interactions. It certainly undermines any pleasure you might get from fitting in if it's on false pretences to begin with.

I'd be a hypocrite to say that masking is all bad. While it has been a struggle to learn to socialise, it has aided my comedy career by making me an observational person who is fascinated by humour and what makes people laugh. It has also made me more empathetic and sometimes I feel I can be more socially perceptive than non-autistic people simply because I have had to learn it from the outside in. A bit like how foreigners who learn a language formally have better grammar than native speakers.

The ability to completely mask and hide how you feel also lends itself to acting or getting through awkward social situations and, frankly, sometimes it is necessary to hide your vulnerabilities. It can be a valuable skill and a very useful option to have available while also being a burden or source of alienation. For example, in a world where autistic people's less visually expressive communication style is misunderstood, it is valuable to be able to do the correct 'face dance'. I have learned that if I calmly use words *only* to express some sort of medical problem, I will struggle to get the seriousness across to some medical professionals. I can see that they register my demeanour as 'calm' even if my words speak of great distress. Rather than seeing masking as a tyrannical suffering imposed by non-autistic people, perhaps it would be healthier to view it as a valuable second language that we can choose to learn.

CHAPTER 4

Why Can't Anyone See How Interesting My Hobby Is?

I can still see the doubt on my friend Kris's face. Kris was my first friend after we had moved to the Isle of Man and he lived nearby so we spent a great deal of time together. He was listening, at my insistence, to an episode of *The Goon Show*. We were eight years old.

The majority of people with autism have special interests. These are topics of interest to us that form part of a 'restricted, repetitive pattern of behaviour, interests or activities', if you go with the current diagnostic criteria, but increasingly the rhetoric is becoming more positive. After all, what's wrong with having an interest? They used to be seen as *only* something autistic people did as an avoidant behaviour, to manage anxiety, that they made autistic people inflexible, antisocial and obsessed. This may well be true of special interests, but not *only* those things – they can be hugely positive and inherently rewarding, maybe leading to a better social life or even a career.

Special interests can function as a way of controlling or navigating a conversation that an autistic person might otherwise find challenging. A lot of us find the world to be needlessly chaotic and loud, and engaging in a special interest can be a source of calm and, say if you're collecting things, a chance to put something in your environment into a logical, familiar order. They're also a great way to block out thoughts and quiet the mind. I certainly find that my brain never stops thinking, maybe can't, and it can become exhausting and tiresome. It can be impossible to block out stress and anxiety. It's like being awake at four in the morning with the last guest of a party who won't leave and won't stop asking you piercing questions about your personal life and then offering their opinion. Imagine that but the living room is in your head and it's forever. Now imagine being able to distract that awful man with, I don't know, an enormous book on Stalingrad. He's reading it quietly and you can sneak off to bed! Generally speaking, the greater the stress or anxiety in your life the more intense the interest can become, since the engaging in the interest is both soothing and avoidant.

You might be sitting back and saying that this just sounds like a hobby! We all have hobbies and interests, don't we? Here we reach the same problem that all psychological diagnoses have that we outlined in the introduction – when is something normal and when is it not?

One of the points of difference between hobbies and special interests is intensity and purpose. When I have a special interest, I go all in. I want to know it all, almost to 'win' it or 'complete it in my own head'. I get irritated with myself when there are things about it I don't know or get wrong, for example. I want to eat it, to own it, to be *one* with it. There's a sort of madness there. In contrast, I would say I play poker as a hobby. I can easily emotionally accept that I don't know everything about poker, I don't really want to learn everything about it and, even though I should, I can't be bothered to read a whole book about it. I am happy to do it as a social thing with my buddies and enjoy the thrill of it all without getting too deep into it. In other words, a hobby. The intensity of a special interest can mean that it completely takes over your brain, it's all you can focus on and it can interfere with daily life. Was it a good idea to get incredibly interested in the fall of Berlin? Sure, maybe, but I can tell you one thing: reading about the harrowing fall of Berlin in 1945 immediately before a gig does *not* put you in a good mental place for comedy.[54] Being deprived of special interests can also cause distress in a way that a hobby does not – I only play poker maybe three times a year. If I wasn't allowed to compulsively research history or write and perform comedy, I think I would go stir-crazy. That's a fairly neat way of illustrating the difference in terms of purpose. I *need* the special interest and I want to become an expert, to finish it. It can also feel too important to just do when you're bored – this thing takes energy.

The level of commitment is another point of difference. I'm very casual about hobbies but a special interest will absorb hours and hours a day, sometimes even to the point where I might forget to drink or eat or sleep. When I loved fantasy novels as a child and young teen I would read them for two

---

54   There are very few successful observational comedy routines about kids on flak guns or Red Army reprisals, although to be fair, *Downfall* parodies were huge online for a long time. Maybe nothing is immune to comedy's dissolving properties.

or three hours a day every day. I absolutely *chewed* through those things, reading through my tiredness, straining to keep my dry, aching eyes open in bed at night, needing *more more more*. I got away with it because what parent would be livid that their kid was reading too much? Only the evil parents from *Matilda*.

There can be a sort of middle ground between hobby and special interest. I think when I was younger, video games were a special interest. I played *Age of Empires II* to the point where I would dream about it. I learned that game inside and out, I can still make the sound effects with my *mouth*, I *lived in the guts* of that thing. It was also a historical game, so double whammy! Two autistic special interest birds with one nerdy stone. God, I loved it. These days, I play videogames mostly casually, often with friends online, and I do it to turn off my brain and relax, to absorb myself into something. So, my special interest has decayed into a mostly-hobby but, thanks to it being a childhood one and therefore formative, retains the soothing, brain-silencing qualities of a special interest. Whereas I cannot honestly say I play poker to relax – quite the opposite.

That brings us to another point of difference: how you approach it. Special interests tend to be antisocial where hobbies are social. There was certainly nothing social about my love of *The Goon Show*, no matter how I tried. Even with Warhammer, on the few occasions I tried to actually play the game or meet others who were interested, I sort of resented the intrusion into my area and felt unhealthily competitive and ashamed of not knowing enough about it. I would have rather just read about it and sat and painted the various models on my own. I felt quite betrayed, in a funny sort of way, that *even* Warhammer would devolve into something social with interactions and tensions and little tribes and cliques. This was supposed to be my *escape* from that![55]

One (entirely subjective, sociological) way of differentiating between hobbies and special interests is the level of specificity and the rarity or how socially accepted it is. I think specificity and rarity have *some* redeeming qualities as points of difference. For example, there is no social reason in modern Britain to become obsessed with *The Goon Show*. That is very specific and very rare. However, I think that the people who know the names, reputations, ages and injuries of seemingly *every fucking footballer* are in possession of some deeply obsessive and specific knowledge. It's just that it's not as unusual and it's socially acceptable. As with anything diagnostic, we reach a troubling paradox: all these things are relative but, at the same time, you know it when you see it.

Unfortunately, some special interests are seen as less appropriate than others. For example, an adult male with a special interest in stuffed animal toys. If an autistic person is unlucky like this, because they don't choose what 'gets them', then they can face a great deal of stigma and social difficulty.

Looking back, I can blame the Port Erin library on the Isle of Man for at least two of my autistic special interests. In South Africa, you only start school the year you turn seven, so when I arrived on the Isle of Man just before my seventh

---

55 I also thought what I often think when I encounter cliquey nerds: you've betrayed your roots. You of *all* people should know how much this kind of thing sucks the joy out of life and you're just reproducing your high school torture chamber? Was your only problem with it that you never got to have a go at the exclusion yourself?

birthday I had never been to school before and was plopped straight into Year 2. I had learned to read in preparation for the move but couldn't write much other than my name. As part of helping me adjust, Mum took us to the local library. On my very first visit I took out *Dark Knights and Dingy Castles*, one of the early *Horrible Histories*, and it lodged in my tiny brain like a crossbow bolt. I already loved knights and castles and Robin Hood – I would sit and watch an Afrikaans-dubbed Robin Hood in South Africa with the level of patience that only a true Merry Man could muster, and this book was a revelation. Reading it made me feel high, giddy, like my brain was a hungry stomach and the book was thick stew being poured into it. I read it in a sort of trance, all that excitement and love on the inside but outside frozen into a statue. I didn't know it then but that was my first taste of hyperfocus *and* a special interest all at once. My complete obsession with history would eventually lead to studying Anglo-Saxon, Norse and Celtic Studies at Cambridge.

The other thing to blame on Port Erin library was the aforementioned *Goon Show* obsession. They had a bank of cassettes you could borrow[56] and among them lay several precious *Goon Show* episodes. The librarian recommended them on the basis that her husband had loved them when he was about my age. When I took them home, sceptically, I found that my dad had also listened to them on the BBC World Service in South Africa. Comedy? That *Dad* knew about? Well, at the very least they would be more interesting than

---

56 Writing that I got into a 1950s radio comedy by going to the library and borrowing *cassettes* makes me feel like a pensioner in a fucking documentary. My God. And our milk came in bottles! Nurse? My pills!

some of the old cassettes we had lying around. We had some kid's story about a cat called Gobbelino, the second half of the score of *Phantom of the Opera*, and a collection of *Famous Five* cassettes that made it sound like the narrator was melting or in slow motion.[57]

I played *The Goon Show* cassettes in my room lying on my bed and they completely rewired my brain. I'd listen to them over and over again. Initially I would fast forward through Ray Ellington's jazz band but eventually I'd listen to that too. I learned all the voices, memorised through repetition scene after scene with which to torture friends and relatives and became convinced that everyone involved deserved a Nobel Prize. It inspired in me an obsessive love of comedy, silly voices and a fascination with how jokes can be constructed, timed and delivered, which would eventually lead to my career as a professional comedian. If you don't like my stand-up or my writing, feel free to direct your ire towards Port Erin library.

I would play *The Goon Show* to my sisters and to any of my friends who would listen. No one I tried this on was ever older than eleven years old and it never worked. I would throw my hands up in delight, crying, 'Isn't that so funny!' only to be met with, at worst, the wail of a bored sister, at best a charitable grimace. The sort of face you pull if someone suggests they might audition for *X Factor* when you know that their singing could only ever be used as a warning. Slowly, far too slowly, I realised that for whatever reason *The Goon*

---

57 In fairness, this did make me weep hot tears of hysterical laughter. The high voice of a mystery-solving child descending into the insane, deep monster voice of an anonymised member of the IRA in a documentary.

Show was a 'me' thing and stopped trying to share it.[58] The same fate eventually befell my stock of historical facts and I kept them to myself like wine in a cellar. I was still confused and irritated, however. After all, my friends and family were *wrong*: *The Goon Show was* funny! Why couldn't they hear what I heard? Why couldn't they see what I saw? I could tell that when they heard one of my historical facts, it didn't deliciously fill a hole in their mind that they didn't know was there, it didn't make them feel like they were one step closer to some sort of incredible all-knowing power. If it was one of my *best* facts, a real pure bred, it would elicit genuine (if mild) surprise and curiosity. Most of them were met with the fake version, which I could always tell, but I took what I could get. I could never shake the nagging sensation that I somehow wasn't communicating the *wonderous nature* of my facts to these damn ingrates, that maybe there was some different way of speaking that they would understand.

So, *The Goon Show* became (and can still be) something I listen to repeatedly over the years to get to sleep or calm myself. I don't just mean nostalgic – I mean it feels like I'm lying on the grass on a warm day in dappled sunlight. The obsessive historical reading, including Wikipedia rabbit holes, is my version of downtime, however. For example, I will do that to keep my brain occupied during any journey of any length.

Special interests come and go, of course, and this can cause problems. For example, just before lockdown I finally read *Tinker Tailor Soldier Spy* and became so obsessed with

---

58 Please admire the iron will, the sheer discipline it took not to write a full extra book-length digression on *The Goon Show* here. Phew!

John le Carré that I read everything he had ever written, much of Graham Greene and a few other spy books and then, during lockdown, wrote my own spy thriller. All jolly good fun I am sure, though I do think I am now on a list for some of the research for the novel. I was trying to determine whether or not a water-based shaped-charge explosive, often used by bomb disposal, would soak the area around it when it blew up. Basically, does the wet bomb that uses water to disarm other bombs make a liquid mess? Or does the water vaporise? I used Google to find and telephone a company that makes the bombs and they were, frankly, suspicious. I told them I was writing a movie because that felt more ... flippant? Than a book? Less sinister maybe, more whimsical. Men who write books have plans and private thoughts, whereas men who write movie scripts are just in it for the pizzazz of it all. The baffled receptionist took my number and said an engineer would ring me back at some point. A week later, an incredibly serious-sounding man rang me at seven in the morning. After confirming that I was the weirdo who got in touch, he got me to repeat my inquiry before saying, firmly but with some regret, that he couldn't tell me anything about the mechanics of the device.

'But it's only a shaped-charge explosive!' I wailed, appealing to the engineer in him. 'It's technology from the Second World War!' I added, another stray historical fact slipping out like spittle.

'That's ... true,' he admitted, sounding surprised. 'But ... nevertheless.' I made some plaintive noises and he said, 'Well, look, I presume you've seen our website? If you just go on there and watch some of our videos of the product in action, you could just take your conclusions from there.'

It wasn't the dream scenario but he was right. Besides, I was already clearly doing a level of research that no normal reader could possibly give a shit about, bar the Tom Clancy-level guys, but those were the very people I wanted to impress and, crucially, the people who tended to read these books. Anyway, I thanked him profusely for his time and did as he said. He was very kind considering I could have just been a lunatic/am a lunatic, delete as applicable.

This, however, brings me onto one of the serious risks of special interests. Intense fixations can be a method of self-soothing initially and naturally grow into an almost-academic (in some cases literally academic) fascination. As a result, there can be cases of autistic people developing obsessions, special interests or hyper focuses on areas that put them in conflict with the law. There are multiple, famous examples of autistic computer hackers whose special interest in hacking or related areas got them into trouble – for example, Gary McKinnon, who committed the largest hack in US military history in his search for evidence of UFOs.

It's not just hacking; there are a 'staggeringly high'[59] number of autistic people on the controversial, anti-terror Prevent scheme here in the United Kingdom, including several children. Now, this isn't to say you cannot get an autistic terrorist, but let's say I had enthusiastically downloaded a manual on shaped-charge explosives from the Second World War in pursuit of making my novel as realistic as possible? I may well be in breach of the law and vulnerable to

---

59   Jonathan Hall QC.

prosecution. We don't choose our special interests, after all, and they are cripplingly addictive and isolating sometimes, especially if you are an already isolated young man with a disability. It would be simple for an autistic person, crippled by anxiety around terrorism, to soothe themselves by endlessly researching how it all works and get themselves into trouble.

It's not just the British government in danger of criminalising autistic traits. At the time of writing, the Australian government uses a tool called Vera-2R that tries to predict how likely someone convicted of terror offences will be to reoffend. The tool considered autistic offenders more likely to reoffend despite there being no empirical evidence of this.[60] In fact, if the original offence was itself the result of a special interest that had grown out of hand, there may have never truly been a terror offence to begin with![61] However, it is true that individuals with autism can be very vulnerable to manipulation, so there is a greater potential for radicalisation – as there is for any group that is disproportionately lonely, spends a lot of time online, feels left out of society and yearns for a system of rules or way of living that can make sense of their lives. I am fortunate to have avoided too crippling a hyperfocus on anything risky or damaging, but I do wonder whether or not I'm on a list somewhere as a 'wet bomb enthusiast'.

As always with neurodivergence, the field of study is undermined by a lack of data. This means that new information will disproportionately change how we see things. I found a

---

60 https://www.theguardian.com/australia-news/2023/may/12/australian-terrorism-prediction-tool-considered-autism-a-sign-of-criminality-despite-lack-of-evidence

61 If someone becomes fascinated with the mechanics of detonators, they are not a terrorist. They have no guilty mind, no *mens rea*, no intent to commit the act and so on. They're just a weirdo.

study on 'Vulnerability to Ideologically-Motivated Violence Among Individuals With Autism Spectrum Disorder' that claims that people with autism are over-represented at 3 per cent of lone actor terrorists compared to a population prevalence of 1.5 per cent.[62] However, the latest population prevalence estimates based on youth diagnoses in the US is 2.8 per cent, well within the margin of error of the lone actor statistic.[63] The study doesn't seem to have considered that you will find more autism in populations where you actually bother to screen them and we will naturally prod the brains of mass killers far more thoroughly than we will prod the brains of, say, millions of children at a time. If the authors of this study had had the more up-to-date information about autism prevalence in the population, there wouldn't have been a section of their study that reinforces a damaging idea about autistic people. Then again, autistic people are vulnerable to manipulation, so their instincts weren't necessarily wrong. Unfortunately, we barely have the data to understand this problem. After all, we barely have the data to fully understand what autism is and how and why it occurs. For now, try not to judge any autistic people you know too harshly on their interests and, my fellow autistics, be careful with what you get into.

In terms of the upside of special interests, I firmly believe

62 Woodbury-Smith, M. R., Loftin, R., Westphal, A., & Volmar, F. R. (2022). 'Vulnerability to Ideologically-Motivated Violence Among Individuals With Autism Spectrum Disorder'. *Frontiers in Psychiatry*, 13:873121. DOI: 10.3389/fpsyt.2022.873121

63 Maenner, M. J., Warren, Z., Williams, A. R. et al. (2023). 'Prevalence and Characteristics of Autism Spectrum Disorder Among Children Aged 8 Years — Autism and Developmental Disabilities Monitoring Network, 11 Sites, United States, 2020'. MMWR Surveillance Summaries; 72(No. SS-2):1–14. DOI: http://dx.doidio.org/10.15585/mmwr.ss7202a1

that they should be encouraged and enabled.[64] Regardless, I think fighting a child's obsession won't help them or you. Why not take a lesson from judo and use the force of your opponent to your advantage? A child who is obsessed with household objects could be diverted into getting fascinated with how they are designed or manufactured, a child obsessed with maps could get into art. After all, my earliest obsessions became my degree and my job, so it's more than possible. There is no reason to ignore the value of special interests and try to force autistic children out of studying something they love when instead you could help them realise the full potential of their special interest.

Special interests can also take the form of collecting and here we enter what you might call classic autism territory – men with trains, Airfix models or Warhammer. Not only men, obviously, but that's the stereotype. In reality, anyone with autism can obsessively collect anything and it's something I have to keep an eye on. I used to build and paint models as a teenager, yes, including Warhammer, but as you will read in Chapter 3, I eventually either outgrew it, or surgically removed it, as it were, in a desperate attempt to seem more sociable. I cannot tell which. However, when I was growing up, I remember saying to someone who I now believe to be autistic as well, 'You know how when you buy one thing that is part of a collectible set of many things and you feel that incredibly powerful urge to keep going?' And they knew exactly what I meant. My more neurotypical friends did not.

---

64 Though maybe not the bomb-making stuff – then again, there are many companies that need engineers to design and make bombs, so ... split the difference? Save it for your twenties, university instead of high school, maybe, like contents insurance or MDMA.

To this day, if I was to buy a pack of football stickers it would lead to a financial disaster. I do not know about football, I do not even really like it, certainly I don't like a lot of the social culture around it ... but one of those packs? Even looking at those stickers by the till of a shop, I can feel a sort of string in my chest being pulled. The closest thing to it I've ever heard is former smokers telling me what it's like when they see someone smoking in a film. A terrible pull towards a delicious abyss. The second I had a few stickers I would feel a sad, lonely hole where all the other stickers in the book should be and that would be that. Online auction wars, compulsive buying of packs, constantly ruminating on how to attain a rare Croatian goalkeeper. It wouldn't even matter that I don't care about the actual football – the stickers would be enough.

This ruinous feeling has also risen in my chest when looking at comic books, Second World War figurines, the lanyards and artist passes for all twelve years of the Edinburgh Fringe I have performed at, every single gig ticket I have ever held, buttons, badges, stickers of any kind, Magic: The Gathering cards, playing cards, Warhammer figurines, chess sets, kitchenware, hardware tools, paints, paintbrushes, canvases and art books, almost any video game and video game achievements and, of course, stamps. I think I would be cripplingly addicted to a few of these were it not for the twin sentinels of my own laziness and my powerful sense of shame and waste when spending money on things. Phew! Sorry, philately! You've lost a potential recruit.

There can be risks in special interests, too. The problem is that they can start to fade, gradually or just suddenly disappear. Let's say you have a special interest in, for example, stamp collecting. You've had it for years, it's part of what bonded you with your grandfather, you made some lifelong friends growing up through doing it and it provides a crucial social opportunity in your adult life because you don't socialise much otherwise. In other words, it's a lynchpin of who you are currently and who you were in the past. If it starts to fade, you can feel it. I've had that feeling with Pokémon before, I think. I definitely remember playing one of the games on my Game Boy and just feeling ... less. Like a drug you've suddenly developed a 20 per cent tolerance for. The thrill is there, kind of, but now it's muffled. You shake it off, everyone gets a little bored of stuff sometimes! So, you try again immediately, or tomorrow, or next week. Still muffled. Then, the week after that, it's like 50 per cent muffled. You're starting to see flaws in it, you're contemptuous of some of it maybe. You feel like this intricate little puzzle that drew you in has been solved and, once a puzzle is completed, it's just a picture. In fact, it's worse than a picture, it's a picture with a bunch of irritating puzzle-y lines criss-crossing all over it. It can be very distressing because you can feel this terrible fading interest while it is happening to you, feel yourself losing something precious.

Luckily for me, Pokémon was just a game I enjoyed playing in private and, ultimately, I had other games. Sure, it felt like a slice of childhood was dying, but that's all right, really. If you're the stamp collector described above, though? That's going to be agony. You're going to feel your natural interest fading even as you talk to your beloved grandfather about stamps, even as you hang out with friends at the pub you made through the philately club. You're going to feel something that has given you years of joy dying in the privacy of your own mind. Worse, you are autistic, so you have a vastly reduced tolerance for being bored and for having to lie or mask socially. You got into stamps to *avoid* boredom and pretending to like things, and now stamp collecting has grown slowly to become the very prison you sought to escape. What's more, you know it will be impossible to explain to your grandfather, to your friends, what has happened. They won't ever understand. They will be baffled and sceptical that such a thing could happen to a person and, inevitably, they will take it personally and be sad. (Even if they weren't going to take it personally, it would probably still be impossible to explain.) So there's guilt in there too, as well as fear. It's a bleak picture I am painting and I admit this is worst-case scenario.

The best-case scenario is that it's just some weird Wikipedia rabbit hole you fell down for a month and you just move on to the next thing seamlessly, losing nothing in the process. Like when I stopped giving a shit about Zoroastrianism and started reading a lot about why American military units always have such high numbers in their identification (the 705th bomber wing? Are there really 704 other bomber wings? There can't be! What's *happening* here?!).

It's also risky to accidentally pursue your special interest as a career. Special interests are often limited in their scope in ways that people do not expect. For example, you might develop a special interest, through anxiety maybe, in cancer, specifically tumours and how they develop. If this happened to you early enough, it could accidentally bias you towards a career in medicine (specialising in oncology?), and by the time you realise that you hate working with, touching or speaking to any of the patients, their families, the fluorescent lights in hospitals, having to mask socially around colleagues and so on, it's too late to back out of your medical career without massively disrupting your life. That's another extreme example but it can and does happen to autistic people.

The best-case scenario is that, via your special interest in tumours, you go along this medical path and you *do* like it and become a somewhat anti-social but incredibly valuable member of the healthcare system. Or maybe you don't deal with patients but you help create tools that can identify tumours much earlier in their formation by identifying unusual cell cluster patterns or whatever. Risks and rewards abound! I do believe that if we could somehow get enough autistic people interested in and in charge of things like national transport infrastructure, we would do very well out of it. Then again, the most efficient way of doing things isn't always the nicest way, or the way people prefer, so that might not be a popular solution.

CHAPTER 5

Sensory Issues

Sensory issues or 'sensory differences' are hypersensitivity *and* hyposensitivity (undersensitivity) to external stimuli. Basically, a set of different experiences and responses that autistic people may have to sight, sound, taste, smell, physical touch, even balance and being able to tell where their body is; it's either an information overload or failure to pick up on information from your environment. It's either way too much or not nearly enough. Sensory issues are very much in the 'processing difficulty' part of autism. Too much information can be highly stressful and create a lot of anxiety or even a meltdown. Just imagine trying to host a busy child's birthday party in an art gallery filled with drunk football fans and you're getting a good idea of why someone might have a meltdown due to environmental stress.

It might seem like there would be no need to diagnose an under- or oversensitivity to something like smell or sound.

After all, some people have a great sense of smell, what about people who work in wine or perfume? Are *they* autistic now? They may very well be. Often when people react to new information about autism they end up accidentally correctly pointing out evidence of autism as opposed to evidence of its absence. They end up like someone throwing up their arms in frustration and saying, 'Oh! So I suppose this means *everyone* at the Trainspotters' Guild could be autistic? Next, you'll be telling me that all my shy friends in the university maths department are autistic too!' My friend, the odds are good.

Stimming can be regarded as an offshoot of sensory issues. After all, you might stim in response to overwhelming sensory input as a way of coping with having such a sensitive sense of hearing or smell. You might also be able to soothe yourself by stimming with interesting textures and that's also part of having an extra-sensitive sense of touch. Sensory differences are mainly a difficulty because we live in a non-autistic world, but they can occasionally provide a solution.

In terms of why it's relevant or worthwhile diagnostically it's time to return to relative intensity. Everything comes down to this, over and over again. Is it bad to have a really good sense of smell? Not necessarily. What if my sense of smell is so over- or undersensitive that it causes me serious distress, social problems, health problems and affects my quality of life? What if I can smell body odour from a hundred metres away? What if I can't smell when food is rotten and keep getting sick? Then it matters. It always comes down to where you are on the bell curve, how far away you are from average. Let's go through sensory issues sense by sense and see how these issues can manifest.

Sight

In terms of sight, for example, you might only be able to focus on parts of something complex, bright or overwhelmingly colourful. I definitely visually seek out details, especially on buildings, and it makes you seem like you're checking the environment for gunmen on behalf of the President. I see people nervously following my eyeline to some particularly ornate balcony and hoping I'm going to explain. I don't – why spoil the fun? Though socially there is a risk in seeming like you aren't listening.

Sensitivity to, and hatred of, fluorescent light is a common autistic trait that I don't fully share but must be absolute hell in the standard work environment. Sensitivity to visual distractions and light, definitely! I can't be sociable in a pub where I can see a television. It does *not matter* what is on the television. I have total and utter cow brain and I will trail off mid-sentence, going *buuuuuuuh*, to look at fun moving bright shapes. I could be trying to warn someone that they are going to be murdered and I would get distracted, and it could be live footage of pensioners playing bowls, it doesn't matter. Very embarrassing that I, as someone who likes to think of himself as a smarty pants, can genuinely be utterly helpless in front of a television or a fruit machine like a literal baby.

It can also mean, say, bad depth perception and clumsiness – hello, high school rugby coach who carefully informed me that I had 'hands like tits'. (He meant my hands were like tits in terms of them being bad at catching. I mean, I presume. I don't think he meant that I had particularly voluptuous, sexy hands. In fairness, I would enjoy a rugby-themed drag act that can catch a rugby ball between her breasts, lots of jokes about rucking and little shorts, poles, am I converting you? etc. – it writes itself! She could be called Scrummy Mummy.)

Sound

Hoooo boy, the big one, for me anyway. Our old friend sound. Undersensitivity could be why some autistic people find that they particularly enjoy very loud, intense music; they may find it relaxing or that it helps them to concentrate. Oddly, I used to be like this. I could only concentrate when drawing for art classes while listening to unreasonably aggressive music at maximum volume. I could also only go to sleep with something playing, maybe late-night radio, something just below my hearing level, murmuring voices ideally, like there were two chatty guards posted outside a thick door to my room. As a child, I was presumed to be deaf by several teachers, which could be a sign of sound processing difficulty, hyperfocus blocking out sounds or just ignoring things I don't want to hear. Impossible to tell!

Oversensitivity to sounds is much more my area. It's extremely difficult for me to concentrate in the wrong environment. I don't need perfect silence, although that would be great, but some days my hearing is at Spider-Man level, if Spider-Man procrastinated for half an hour in trying to figure out where that high-pitched noise was coming from and discovered it was literally the sound of electricity in his wall.[65] It's not just that my hearing is good enough or sensitive enough to hear things like that, it's that

---

65 A very low-stakes and quite unsettling adventure for Spider-Man but one that, statistically, *will* be made into a movie.

SENSORY ISSUES

I can't seem to block out the sounds. I can't stop my brain from fully tuning in to the mundane conversation happening twenty metres away, or block out the loud radio show talking in the background. Even lyrics from a song playing in the background can shatter any attempt at concentration. It's not ideal when you're a freelancer who tries to work in cafés, places that are, let's face it, famous for ambient music and conversation.

All that's just the tip of the aural iceberg for me, however. The real issue is misophonia, or hatred of sounds. Considering how common misophonia seems to be, it's crazy to me that it isn't even something you can be formally diagnosed with – as I type this, it's being underlined in red as if it doesn't exist. It seems social media has helped the huge number of sufferers figure out they are not alone. If you don't know what I mean by hatred of sounds, lucky you and let me explain.

There are certain sounds that, when I hear them, fill me with a sudden anger and hatred. I cannot fucking *stand* them and I immediately have to deal with this anger in a moderate, healthy and often invisible way. When I say they make me angry, I don't mean I click my tongue and say, 'Oh, how rude!', I mean they make me angry the way you see guys get angry after they've been shoved in the chest in a pub. It's sudden, involuntary and instinctive and the sound feels like some sort of personal assault.

Some of the sounds that make me angry make a kind of social sense. I cannot *stand* the sound of someone eating or drinking noisily. I don't mean someone eating something vaguely crunchy as best they can with their mouth closed. I mean anyone eating with their mouth open, lip smacking, tongue slapping off the roof of their mouth, ricocheting like a disgusting pink bullet, wet mouth sounds, slurping drinks (yes, even hot ones, just fucking *wait*)[66] and even when people clank metal cutlery against their teeth.

How does that feeling not make you want to shoot yourself!? Metal on *exposed bone*? Like at the *dentist?* Scraping the food off your fork with your poor teeth instead of just using your damn lips? Clacking your teeth as you somehow try to *bite* soup off a spoon?! I have just realised that I have been writing with fully gritted teeth just imagining it.

The eating sounds thing is insane to me. Eating with your mouth open and noisily is supposed to be dealt with when you are a tiny child, isn't it? Did these people's parents do it and pass on the curse to their young like a slurpy Dracula? Were the parents just too knackered to tell their kid to stop eating like a mad animal? It's such an incredible imposition to me, to force me to hear your intimate sounds like that. The level of sensitivity is high, I admit; I can genuinely hear someone eating crisps with their mouth open from the other end of a train carriage. I also reserve a special place in hell for people sucking their fingers after eating something, an unthinkably Freudian act that I would be disappointed to see take place during a bout of cannibalism, much less at a Nando's. Look, the flavour and tiny amount of excess sauce on your fingers just didn't make it into your mouth this time. For now you must accept the loss and clean your hands with a wipe and not using your tongue like a dog with a wound.

I'm also really not a fan of 'enjoyment noises' when people

---

66 To say nothing of those people who do that satisfied little GASP after they take a big sip of a drink. They sort of smack their lips once and go pu-AHHHHH. Oh? *REFRESHED ARE WE? LOVELY DRINK, WAS IT?* I want to scream as I smoosh their can of Diet Coke in my fist like the Incredible Hulk.

are eating or drinking. I find them revolting and perverse. Don't get me wrong, a vague 'mm, wow' is perfectly fine, but people who moan through a mouthful of food, eyes rolling about like a wild horse, groaning and pushing more food in while still chewing are intolerable. The whole thing would be unacceptable if it was someone, say, sitting in a comfy chair, groaning, whispering, grunting, saying, 'Oh *God*, oh *fuck*' while they rubbed their arse on the cushion, so why is it OK when you're eating a wet hamburger?

I am aware, hosting as I do a podcast with my Chinese Malaysian friend Phil Wang, that these are vaguely Eurocentric cultural mores. Over our years of friendship I have grown tolerant of the fact that Phil drinks water like a cartoon character, with gulps that sound like sound effects that you could download for 99p, something called 'big_swallow.wav'. I also accept, as a brutal pragmatist, him pointing out that if you don't slurp some of the soup with your noodle soup you just end up eating plain noodles and then an enormous bowl of soup one by one, as opposed to actually eating noodle soup. I don't like it but I'll accept it. So, there is some vulnerability to logic in there somewhere, or at least an ability to make concessions, but it's rare. The chewing stuff might be something to do with having it hammered into me when I was young just how incredibly *rude* it is? I definitely got my cutlery vs teeth horror from my mother, so it can certainly be passed on.

These sounds filling me with rage could at least be explained away by some extreme version of good manners. I could claim to belong to some kind of etiquette Taliban[67] and

---

67 Neat caves.

insist that it was all just about politeness. Unfortunately, that's not quite the case.

One of the more niche sounds that makes me furious is, for example, the very loud, weird ringing sound a phone call makes when someone makes a phone call through their car. To clarify: someone is in a parked car with their phone hooked up through their car speakers so that they can make and receive calls while driving. This means the sound of their call connecting and ringing blasts through the speakers. This means it is audible, say, from my first-floor flat. I have no idea what exactly it is about this, maybe because it's a sort of mega, car-powered version of how rude it is when people do loudspeaker phone calls on public transport?[68] Maybe it's because it makes me feel like *I* am making a phone call, which I often do not enjoy doing? Either way, when it happens I am utterly enraged and it is unfortunate because it seems I am the only person who can even hear this sound, much less hear it through glass. People don't react well when you suddenly become enraged and say things like 'The ringing!' while stomping over to a window. It gives the impression that you are close to committing the kind of crimes that get you on Netflix.

Equally demented is my loathing of people using diminutive or patronising words. By this, I tend I mean abbreviations like brekkie for breakfast, choccy for chocolate, din dins for dinner and so on.[69] I hate them and react worst to them when they are

---

68 Something that also fills me with rage but is a normal rage-inducing sound from what I can tell. I think if you are the kind of person who makes loudspeaker phone calls on public transport, you are a symptom and cause of the decay of the social contract and genuinely make society worse, every day. In a small way, yes, but a small way that adds up the way that droplets of water can erode granite.

69 Genuinely irritated by typing that.

spoken, though written down they still irritate. Also, any words that are the sort of words you might coo at a baby like yummy, scrummy, tummy, num, nom, hubby; any and all baby talk is *out*. If I'm lucky enough to have kids I will be speaking to them in a chillingly formal manner, the vibe will be very much Alfred and tiny Batman. For some reason I am also infuriated by what I call '*Beano* words', a mostly British phenomenon that infects the output of politicians and journalists. When you are infected by *Beano* talk you speak like Hugh Laurie's character from *Blackadder*. After you are infected, you will never drink champagne, only 'quaff' or 'guzzle' it. You will never eat food again, only 'scoff' or 'munch' it. An article about some fancy political dinner will describe the guzzling of champagne or the scoffing of canapés as though describing the looting of a palace, or as though pointing out that political dinners tend to be quite fancy is an insight. It is also used to patronise the general public, who won't be told 'save money by switching to a more energy-efficient television and spend the extra cash on treats' but rather that they should 'bin their leccy-guzzling tellybox and scoff choccies instead!' It's embarrassing for the writer *and* the reader. There's something horribly manic in its cheerfulness; it's the way you'd try to tell a toddler with a gun to put it down.

Suffice to say, I am well aware how completely insane I sound. Most people wouldn't have the energy to have this many opinions on this many types of sound, much less the energy to actively be infuriated by them. I would point out that I also feel like I can't spare the energy, it's just that I have no choice. Though in fairness when I am completely exhausted I will let any number of scrummy choccies get munched in my presence without reacting, like one of those drugged tigers people take selfies with.

I know a few people who also hate almost exactly the same things as me so there is some sort of pattern here. Maybe it's something to do with revolting against the feeling of being patronised, or it gives us flashbacks to being constantly misunderstood when we were very young ourselves. There's certainly room there for some romantic, Proustian idea, but it won't change the reaction. The irritation is instant, I'm afraid, and not a decision. What *is* a decision is not letting yourself react and not letting it get to you, so you can learn to be Zen about these noises and no one will ever know. However, they need to know if they are going to stop, so that may not be useful, and it is tiring and sometimes breeds resentment to just constantly swallow your irritation internally and never express it.

Taste

I cover a lot of this in the chapter about autistic relationships with food, but in essence it's our old, eternal companion in autism: too much or not enough. An undersensitive sense of taste can lead to cravings or a need for very strong-tasting or spicy food. Some autistic people may even engage in pica, eating or putting non-edible things like stones in their mouth. An oversensitive sense of taste can lead to autistic people preferring to eat bland, plain foods like unflavoured chips or plain white bread. There can also be a strong texture aspect to the revulsion, the same issue that many people would have with maybe some unexpected gristle. That, but for something more surprising, like the feeling of all those nobbly little tree bits on broccoli.

I have a varied palate now but when I was a child the idea of combining, say, some gravy, some roast beef and some potato on your fork and eating it all in one mouthful made me want to glue my mouth shut. How could anyone *stand* to mix such flavours! It was like watching someone putting a scoop of mint chocolate ice cream onto their fish and chips. Sensory differences in taste are the start of a domino effect that can lead to much worse health outcomes in the short and long term for autistic people. You can definitely get away with only eating very bland foods but it will be tough to eat a healthy diet when the only food you can eat is beige – just imagine eating like a hungover teenager but forever.

Smell

An undersensitive sense of smell can be the cause of some obvious hygiene issues in terms of body odour, but it can also be risky in terms of being able to discern if food has gone off or there is a gas leak, for example. When I had Covid, I lost my sense of smell completely for weeks. It was bizarre. Even with lockdown limiting my socialising to wandering a near-empty supermarket with other mask-wearers, I found I was still paranoid that I smelled either bad or too much of deodorant.

I would say that, brief Covid interlude aside, I am in possession of a pretty sensitive nose. As a child, being taken into any shop that heavily featured perfume counters, scented candles or odorisers was hell. I would feel a delirious car sickness almost immediately and that, combined with the boredom and the fact that I was *trapped* in a world of *stink*, made me want to *flip out*. All kids have tantrums but not because they're trying not to throw up from being near some bath bombs. I'd never had McDonald's until I was five years old and we visited my Uncle Mike in the United States. I leaned over the brown paper bag, opened it, sniffed, said, 'It smells' and didn't eat any. Uncle Mike made a joke about my fine taste, which I think is often the adult reaction to a particularly spooky little freak. More seriously, if your sense of smell is that sensitive it could cause or contribute to issues around using the loo or socialising. For example, having a strong negative reaction to someone's perfume. A word to the wise: you generally won't win people over by *recoiling* from them.

Touch

If your sense of touch is undersensitive you might over-apply pressure in a hug or holding onto someone else. This can be an issue, especially with children – a kid might not know their own strength and be blamed for it but be sincere when they say they didn't do it deliberately. Some autistics even have a high pain threshold – I am not one, sadly for my sporting career.

Apparently, undersensitivity could be behind the appeal to autistic people of having heavy objects on top of them. I know it sounds like woodlouse behaviour, but it is true. I remember as a kid finding it oddly satisfying or comforting to be weighed down by a heavy object if I was lying on the floor. If you spend lots of time online (and most autistic people do), you'll see a

SENSORY ISSUES

lot of talk about weighted blankets and their appeal for the autistic community. I was sceptical until I went through a phase of extremely low-quality sleep and bought one as an experiment. I bought the heaviest one, being an incredibly heavy man myself, and this enormous package arrived in the post, hauled to my door by a postman who must've thought it was a prank. Inside was a blanket made of what seemed to be multiple thick, interacting layers of different artificial fabrics. In between these layers, secured by some ingenious method, were heavy ... beads? Little weights? Spread evenly all over the surface area of the blanket. It takes quite an effort to haul this thing over yourself. It feels like it might be bulletproof.

Reader, it was a revelation. I immediately felt relaxed, comfortable and safe. Something about it made me immediately sleepy, which is not normal for me. I would say that my brain ends every day by throwing a kind of commemorative jubilee where all of my future concerns and all of my past shames perform a show together. The weighted blanket also seemed to massively increase the *depth* of my sleep. The other day I thought I'd use it to have an afternoon nap. In hindsight this was a reckless show of hubris, to use such a mighty power for something as mundane as a nap. You wouldn't wield Excalibur to cut your *cheese*! I awoke to the sound of my alarm two hours later like I had been kidnapped and drugged: I had no idea where I was, what day, nothing. A shining coat of drool coated the side of my face, my eyes were shrivelled little bumholes and I had to clamber out of bed like a zombie forcing its way from the grave. Never again. I have learned to fear and respect the weighted blanket and use it only at night.

Oversensitivity to touch can take some surprising forms.

WHY CAN'T I JUST ENJOY THINGS?

Long before I was diagnosed I knew the (not necessarily correct) stereotype that autistic people don't like hugging. This was one of a constellation of reasons why I didn't think I could be autistic, because I think hugs are great. Instead of being hyper-specific, the diagnostic question should have been more like 'is there a common form of affectionate touch that you strongly dislike?'. When I understood this, I immediately thought of how much I hate holding hands. For some autistics it's also intolerable to be touched lightly, especially on the forearms. It feels very invasive. Handholding is something that I don't like the feeling of inherently – it makes me feel like I don't have hands anymore, like if I needed to use my hands I couldn't. Even as a kid, I would refuse to wear gloves to the point where I would attempt for as long as possible to make snowballs without them and only the agony of my rapidly purpling fingers would convince me that this was a gloves job. Hating things on your feet and hands is another autistic thing, it turns out. I disliked shoes as a kid and frankly, I'd wear sandals every day if I could.

Handholding also filled me with social anxiety: how long are we holding hands for? What's the best way to do this in terms of grip? What if we have sweaty hands? What if someone walks towards us, what's the plan then? Do we break hands and let them through the middle? If so, do the hands rejoin or are we done now? Some of you might be reading this and screaming, 'Just enjoy it!' and I understand – but I don't enjoy it. So I can't. There's also the added fear of 'Oh God, I hate doing this, but I can't *not* do it. That would be bad. And I also can't admit I hate it or display even a *single sign* of discomfort or impatience or resentment, because that would be *really* bad.' If someone likes you and wants to hold your hand, you just have to do it. I learned that the hard way. They really don't like it if you go all awkward and ask if you maybe could not. They will presume that your embarrassment isn't shame at your own failure to be a Nice Normal Romance Man, they will presume you do not want to be seen with them. It is also unwise to try to convince someone you just hate holding hands because either they think you're making it up and dislike that you are lying or they believe you and dislike that you are clearly a stone-hearted brute who dislikes lovely things.

This is another argument in favour of diagnosis. Now that I have my diagnosis, it enables me to explain to my partner that I would rather not hold hands, or whatever your sensory difference might be, without there being as much blame, shame or misunderstanding.

In terms of textures, I have fortunately avoided issues with the textures of most foods, although I admit I still harbour a certain horror for that last stubborn bit of albumen resisting the heat of the pan, wobbling there on top of the cooked egg white like a sneeze. My touch-based sensory issues were mainly to do with clothing, often school uniform. This isn't uncommon, even in neurotypicals – in fact, there are some examples that I think are universal. Surely we can all agree that there is nothing more hideous than a rough, scratchy clothing label flapping and poking at the back of your neck? Surely there isn't a human being alive who could stand the awful jumbly feeling of having a sleeve rumpled up around your elbow underneath a larger sleeve? Cutting off the circulation to your forearm and making your sleeve all lumpy? Well, just imagine that feeling when an autistic person talks about a sensory issue with clothing and you will be empathising in no time.

I hated the feeling of anything restricting my forearms and hands, like gloves as described above but also sleeves. In particular, the ends of the sleeves. For some reason, the primary school jumper of a British child has sleeve-endings so tight they could function as handcuffs. The base of the jumper and neck was similarly restrictive. It's as if the nation expects their children to be somehow watertight, or perhaps capable of inflation. I would try to lessen the problem by stretching the sleeve cuffs over my fists to loosen them but then you would get in trouble for 'ruining your uniform'. I also tend to hate the feeling of wearing jumpers over shirts. Something about feeling the layers interact, one fabric skidding over another when you move around. The jumper tightly restricting and rumpling up the looser shirt fabric underneath, ugh. That feeling of restriction and textural weirdness would make me want to flail about and, in an ideal world, peel the jumper off my body via the head using paws and feet like a dog forced into a costume. However, this is not the behaviour of the ideal schoolboy, and so I had to sit, gently vibrating with tension in my tight, scratchy uniform, and focus on fractions or Tudors or ancient Egypt, staring jealously at the loose robes.

Balance

Autism is such a highly variable condition that even people with the condition will be completely unaware of some possible elements of having it. I never imagined, for example, that the reason so many autistic people may rock back and forth, swing or spin around could be to get some sensory input from an undersensitive sense of balance. I knew that autistic people did it but I associated these movements with an emotional response to something (which it may be).

In hindsight, I'm on Team Oversensitive once again. An oversensitive sense of balance means being crap[70] at sports, car sickness and apparently difficulty with activities where 'the head is not upright or the feet are off the ground'. I just read that sentence on the website of the National Autistic Society and the thing with doing extensive research into your own condition is that you are constantly met with revelations that make sense of your life. That sentence was one of those revelations. Whenever some aspect of physical education or, as an adult, a personal training session involves lying on a mat and doing something, my brain just goes *phut* and stops working. I fall down, I forget how many reps of an exercise I have done, I look like a slow motion video of someone hurting themselves trying to breakdance. For my whole life, up until I read that sentence, I have been getting irritated at myself for my stupid brain getting all hot and slow and weird when I try to do things on the mat and, now that I've read that there is a chance it's just something inherent, I can let myself off the hook a little bit. Should I need the results of medical research in order to be kinder to myself? OK, no, but it's a lot easier when some of the confusing mystery of *why* is removed from the equation.

Car sickness is another bullseye, but I'm something of an expert when it comes to feeling sick in a car. As a child in

---

70   Or, at least, crap*per*.

South Africa I could manage to feel car sick when sitting in the back of a vehicle travelling at a constant speed along a perfectly straight African highway. Now *that's* talent. When we moved to the Isle of Man, it was nothing but winding country lanes, dense hedges and forests on either side – so you can never do the trick where you look at the horizon – highly variable speed limits and sharp bends that create a lot of great opportunities for lurching stops and starts. When my mum took me into Douglas, where the shops were, it was about twenty-five minutes to drive there and park. This was more than enough time for me to go from reluctant but healthy child to Victorian ghost boy. It must have been quite a sight: my mum trying to run errands while dragging along a little boy so visibly green with nausea that it must have looked like a woman was teaching a reluctant goblin how to shop. The great thing about car sickness is that it lasts for a few hours, too, so I began to associate going to the shops and running errands with all-day nausea, which certainly didn't improve my attitude.

However, I certainly didn't need no fancy website to tell *me* I'm not good at sports. At least, in terms of balance. I definitely remember falling over a lot as a kid, tripping, bumping into things. This also crosses over with another slightly niche autistic sensory difference: proprioception! This is your awareness of where your body is in space – not literal space, that's probably 'astroproprioception' – but space relative to other things around you. It's also your awareness of how different body parts are moving. This means autistic people can end up bumping into people or standing too close to them because they find it harder to judge or sense distances.

This, combined with a possible social incomprehension of the importance of some aspects of personal space, can lead to yet more social difficulties and misunderstandings. As a kid, my parents seemed to spend half their energy telling me to be more aware of people around me. I was constantly in front of people, behind people, bumping into people, standing in doorways and so on. I was a living hazard perception test. I think this is why it makes me so angry when adults lack that sort of awareness and stand in my way, blocking corridors chatting or imposing themselves into my personal space on a train. After all, we hate in others what we have eliminated, or seek to eliminate, in ourselves.

I am very lucky that I had my parents, as well as the general social environment of school, to slowly get better and better at proprioception and finally stop bumping into things, tripping up and irritating people. At the time, we blamed it on me growing and just generally being a giant teenager and therefore clumsy. Looking back, there were plenty of giant, athletic, perfectly balanced teenagers who didn't fall down almost at random, but it was nice to have something to blame at the time. Oversensitive proprioception could lead to difficulties with fine motor skills, fiddly things like shoelaces or buttons, and I think I can safely say, thinking back with pride at the genuinely eerie level of tiny detail I was able to paint onto my Warhammer figurines, that I was not affected in this way.

Miscellaneous

I have no idea how to categorise the following sensitivities – they are utterly bizarre – but I feel it would be dishonest not to include them. Myself and a close friend who is very likely to be autistic share the following: a profound sensitivity to certain combinations of colours and a profound sensitivity to historical study. I will do my best to explain these, beginning with the colour sensitivity.

Certain combinations of colours make my friend and I feel nauseous, genuinely physically sick. It is rare, but it can happen.[71] They aren't the same combinations for each of us but they are similar, in my opinion. On the Isle of Man, there is an independent petrol station in Peel that has a logo that makes me feel sick as a dog when I look at it; it's a revolting combination of a very particular blue, yellow and red and I've no idea why I hate it so much. I showed a picture of it to everyone in my family and they had no clue what I was on about; I sent a pic to this friend of mine and he instantly got it. So, if certain colour combinations make you want to throw up, you are not alone.

The sensitivity to historical study, if that even belongs under sensory issues (though it does evoke a very physical reaction), is more abstract. My friend messaged me and asked me, 'Do you ever get it sometimes where you think about certain aspects of history and the breadth of it gives you a brief moment of feeling physically sick?' He then told me about how he had been reading an article about Romanes IV Diogenes of the Byzantine Empire and, upon seeing a drawing of him from the period, 'got a sudden attack of violent nausea from my lack of knowledge of the person,

---

71 Dr Linda Buchan includes this sort of colour sensitivity in her 'sensory checklist' as she has found it is a 'relatively common thing' – Buchan, Dr L., 2024. Voice note to author, 9 January.

period, circumstances and style of drawing'. I couldn't have agreed with him more. I had this exact thing only the other day when I skimmed a Wikipedia article on scapulimancy (divination using shoulder bones) in Shang dynasty China. As I simultaneously came across so many things that I'd never heard of at once (scapulimancy, the Shang dynasty, the idea of divination being incredibly powerful in Chinese society over thousands of years, the sheer timescale of Chinese history [Shang dynasty being over a thousand years before Christ]) and the awful, yawning hole of my total ignorance of *almost all of it* ... It was too much to take in. I had a similar reaction in the British Museum to seeing an ancient Egyptian pot from 5600 BCE – it hit me all at once that this pot was as old as *three full Christianities.* That so long ago there was someone exactly like me using containers for olive oil or whatever. The distress is some combination of the sheer infinite vastness of human history (even the little we have recorded is too vast to take in even in a thousand lifetimes), the guilt and stress I feel of not knowing, my instinctive Gollum-like *need* to know, the horror of how much effort it would take to properly academically understand it all, the stress and injustice of how much is forgotten, the awareness that if we were to try and remember it all we would forfeit our present to some extent ... the sheer impossibility of it! It's too much, I need to lie down, look away, put it out of my mind. Even trying to describe it has given me a headache.

It's definitely the *fanciest* and most pretentious part of my autism – to be so in awe of history it makes me want to clutch my head and be sick – but there's nothing to be done. I've read about similar reactions from autistic people to things like music, or mathematics, or owls, or what have you, so I figured I should include it in case any other 'scale of history' freaks were reading.

Coping methods

It would be great to be able to make your sense of taste, smell, hearing or whatever less sensitive, like adjusting the volume on a speaker but, unfortunately, the best way to cope is to remove the stimuli. Without removing the stimuli, the only way I have ever coped with sensory issues is by being able to temporarily switch off or ignore the part of my brain that cares, but it uses a huge amount of energy and can be very unpleasant and would lead to burnout over a long period of time. Removing or blocking out the stimuli is the only way to cope that isn't masking or suffering.

Noise-cancelling headphones are a *godsend.* Unfortunately, they are extremely expensive, but good-quality ear plugs are affordable and can block out a lot of infuriating sounds. You might feel ridiculous putting ear plugs in to get through the day, but part of autistic self-advocacy is no longer judging yourself for giving yourself what you need.

Don't feel embarrassed about researching which clothes are made from tolerable fabrics or wearing clothing that maybe isn't perfectly formal or neat (if you can get away with it).

In terms of stimming, there is an ever-increasing range of toys designed for adults to stim with, like wristbands or necklaces or just little rubbery doo-hickeys that you can fiddle with. It is difficult to unlearn the shame of needing or enjoying these things but it's worth it. Non-autistic people need all sorts of things to make it through life, so why not treat yourself to a squishy keychain thing? Or get a rubber band from the stationery cupboard. Whatever you need.

Stop feeling bad about leaving a room if someone is eating smelly food or wearing a grandma's worth of perfume. Try to learn what situations cause issues for you. It'll take work to log enough sensory issues and their triggers, but once you've done the work you'll be better able to avoid difficult scenarios in the first place. Basically, like all good advice, it boils down to an infuriating cliché: be yourself, be kind to yourself.

CHAPTER 6

Why Can't You See That I am Correct?

Autism seems to lead to a very 'black and white' approach to life. Autistic people often have extremely defined ideas of good or bad, or right and wrong, and either have a hard time seeing or refuse to accept the shades of grey that may be present. It seems to be part of the overall 'rigidity' of thinking that is present in autism; like the rigid approach to eating or wearing the same thing every day.

The rigidity can lead to a love of or a need for routine. Routine is an important way to reduce anxiety. For example: if you are compelled to view everything as either brilliant or horrific, you will construct a routine that avoids all of the horrific stuff, whatever that may be. You hate crowded buses, so you deliberately take a longer, maybe more expensive route to work. However, this makes you more tired as you have to get up earlier, so you make sure to have coffee early in the day.

One day you get up early but your route has to change,

maybe there are roadworks, so you get to work too quickly having taken the faster, more crowded bus. Now you're too early and all freaked out from the bus, so with nothing to do you have a coffee, but then you need to have your routine coffee as well even though you don't need it, so you get overcaffeinated and crash hard around lunch. All of this is making you ratty. Because you are in a bad mood, and you know that you're bad at hiding emotions, you strategically stay silent in a meeting in order to avoid making a bad impression. However, it occurs to you that the silence *itself* could be seen as negative. You know that you can't ask, so you sit and agonise over this quandary all day. Because you are a black and white thinker, you either succeeded at hiding your bad vibes OR you ruined your career. Nothing in between.

When I say 'view something as horrific' I don't mean normal dislike, I mean you feel it at an animal level right in your guts. You panic, you flail around for a solution, you consider cancelling your plans, consider asking for compassionate leave. In short, you react utterly disproportionately and instinctively, like you would to an *actual* catastrophe. This is not simply a case of the Mondays, though viewing it as such could help you work logically through the panicked thoughts the stress is causing. You can breathe and say, 'Based on how life seems to work for everyone else, this *isn't* a disaster'.[72]

Black and white thinking and logic can make it difficult

---

72 However, because you are autistic, you know that you often get things wrong. All the social signals you thought you knew at some point have been shown to have other meanings, so you are never, ever free of uncertainty. There is always a nagging feeling in the back of your mind that maybe, actually, this *is* one of those situations where you've ruined everything. Statistically, there has to eventually be a really bad one! Oh, logic, I thought you were my ally!

to accept that you are wrong or that you misunderstood something. I definitely went through an incredibly irritating phase growing up where I simply could not accept that I was wrong about something, or that my assumption had been wrong. It wasn't that I lived in denial, it was that my perspective was that if I could be wrong when, only moments before, I had been so certain and confident, then maybe I could always be wrong? Maybe every single time I have ever felt and ever will feel certain and confident and sure of something, it's completely wrong? It could be! Oh God! At some level, my mind just went 'Well, we can't go on like that, we'd go insane' and so formed this enormous protective wall around the idea of being wrong. I'm still not great at admitting I was wrong about something but I'm far, far better than I was and it gets easier every time.

Often, I feel as though the being wrong part is unfair if I had perfectly logical, well-informed reasons for being wrong. For example, let's say that I presumed someone from southern Wales spoke Welsh, having met lots of people from northern Wales who spoke Welsh. If I didn't know that speaking Welsh was generally more of a northern Welsh thing (but not entirely), I would feel like it was fair enough of me to assume that a southern Welsh person spoke it too. This was a real scenario; I think what offended me was the impatient and frustrated tone of the southern Welsh person who corrected me. They were certainly annoyed that I presumed they spoke Welsh. Obviously, there are all sorts of valid reasons they are frustrated that have nothing to do with me: they are tired of explaining Welsh things to non-Welsh people, they are tired of having their Welsh identity invalidated because, through no fault of their own, due to historical factors, they don't speak Welsh, they are used to speaking to people who are rude about Wales and are worried or assume that the person in this situation will be rude too. Maybe their identity is also based on a certain level of rivalry or hostility to people from northern Wales and so they are keen to present their version of Welshness as superior. There could be any number of reasons and these days I presume innocence when someone gets ratty over something; I try to imagine their good reasons and keep my ego out of it. But in this situation I think I interpreted their somewhat harsh tone as a personal rebuke. It was as though they were saying, 'No, you *idiot*, you've *completely misunderstood* something *obvious to any thinking person*, you *should* have known this, you have *no* good reasons for your assumptions. I am going to haul you in front of the *Eisteddfod* and have you ritually killed.'

I get offended because, although I was wrong, and even ignorant, I feel I had some valid reasons for coming to the conclusion I did (and don't see why or how I have earned this contempt. Contempt that I am likely imagining or projecting). The situation deteriorates and no one ends up happy! Fundamentally, part of my response is an attempt to ensure the other person didn't think that I was stupid or illogical. This is part of autism where it is hard to separate nature and nurture. Do I have this attitude because of something inherent, genetic or physically happening in my brain? Or is it that throughout my life neurotypical people have found my opinions, behaviour and desires to be baffling or too different from theirs, and so I have had to constantly justify myself or defend my thinking?

WHY CAN'T YOU SEE THAT I AM CORRECT?

If I don't explain myself, I learned as a child, people will assume it is because I am either stupid or wilfully ignorant or rude, and I am not. My brain goes 'I definitely have good reasons that are internally consistent for being, thinking or doing what I am being, thinking or doing. Maybe if I explained them, people would understand. They would realise it's a big misunderstanding! I swear I'm not stupid!' More selfishly, maybe then they would think I was clever, once they understood my reasoning. I have worked for years to train myself to get over this and admit when I am wrong in a light and breezy manner. This work was mainly via academia because, especially as a child or teenager, you will be wrong a lot in your studies, and I was too much of a nerd not to respect that process. Also, if you flip out over being wrong, people don't want to hang out with you, which is good motivation. It was never that I was unaware that these qualities were negative, it was more that I just couldn't seem to stop myself.

These days I do my best to present myself as someone who only asks questions and rarely makes statements. People love answering questions and they hate arguing with statements. Questions are complimentary to the giver (a curious person who does not assume) and the receiver (interesting, worthy of questions). For example, asking someone at a party if their job is stressful, as opposed to saying, 'Stressful!' when they tell you their job and then hurriedly having to justify your perspective on their life when they didn't even ask for it and all you were doing was trying to Have Something To Say. Much easier to exist as some kind of wandering podcast host, endlessly interviewing people.

People are very interesting if you give them a chance and

sometimes the things they tell you are astonishing, or even deeply personal. I think it's because of how few people feel like anyone is interested in them, or anything they have to say, so they never get to feel heard. Someday I think someone is going to confess a murder to me and I'll just end up nodding and asking them 'did it feel illegal at the time?' I admit that this behaviour is a form of masking, but I think it's more the type of masking that a normal person does at parties, or close to it. When I am extremely tired, or maybe drunk, or the issue being discussed is very important to me, I can slip up and be blunt, black and white, fact-obsessed and so on. This can cause social issues but by keeping an eye on my tiredness levels and making sure I don't take things people say too seriously I can wobble along acceptably. (I've also cultivated a circle of extremely logical, thick-skinned friends who enjoy serious, fact-based discussions.)

If everything is either the best or the worst thing ever, you might have some intense emotional reactions where it isn't appropriate. The first time I realised that I had some excessive reactions to things – and the effect this could have on others – I was eighteen. The Isle of Man is a fairly hard-drinking place to grow up and some friends and I used to meet at an ambitiously Cuban-themed bar in the main town, Douglas. They sold some mixed drinks and cocktails that we thought of as *muy delicioso*, as they say on the Isle of Man. God knows if we were old enough but I think we were, as I was always a complete wuss about pretending to be legal drinking age, despite looking like a post-grad as a fifteen-year-old. We would take turns to buy massive, sickly, neon pitchers and, when it came to my round, I couldn't find the twenty-pound note I had taken out for this exact purpose. It wasn't in any of my pockets – the system had failed![73] 'Oh, for FUCK's *SAKE*,' I said, furiously rifling my pockets like I'd lost my passport. In that moment of anger, I noticed some of my friends' faces fall and one said something along the lines of 'Uh oh' or maybe 'Here we go'. I was furious for a few minutes, muttering about how this could be *possible.*

Eventually, I found I had eccentrically put it into the top pocket of my shirt. You know that thing where sometimes you decide to put your keys in the one pocket you've never used in your life? To give them a little holiday? 'Here we go!' I exclaimed, immediately fine again, no trace of the former bad mood, but I saw that for my friends the legacy of the bad mood remained. One of them even said something like, 'Thank God' with what you might call *a little too much feeling.* I was ashamed. Not only was this behaviour of mine clearly not the sort of thing people enjoyed on a night out, but it was, judging by everyone's practised reactions and the fact that none of them commented on the situation as in any way unusual, *clearly something I was known for.* The shame! The pain of realisation and the agony of being *known* for your *flaws*! I immediately resolved to keep an eye on this part of myself from now on, adding it to the seemingly endless list of repair jobs generated by the ancient, creaking house of my personality.

I definitely improved after that but it certainly didn't go away. I can still flip out at computers or printers and, under extreme duress, go full-on Basil Fawlty if something completely fucks up in a way that I cannot fix, blame on anyone or should

---

73 See executive dysfunction, Chapter 11, for more on The Pocket System.

have seen coming. I generally try to reserve these cathartic bursts for when there is no one else around and they are often video game-inspired.[74]

I once had a girlfriend who was a very lovely, emotionally receptive person but this was not an ideal combo with my way of expressing myself. I remember once I was recording something for a project she was working on, some narration, and I lost my temper with some audio-editing software and whispered. 'For *fuck's sake.*' She took it personally and was quite upset. I think she felt guilty that I was putting perhaps more effort than she'd expected into helping, and guilty for asking for help, so she drew a straight line from her need to my bad mood. From my perspective, she was being bizarre – it was just the audio software being annoying! Can't you logically see that it has nothing to do with you? But we were not living in logic town, I'm afraid. We were in Emotionsville and I was parked illegally, so I had to work quite hard to clear the bad vibe I had accidentally created.

I've become good at suppressing these reactions, but the long-term effects, or rather side effects, of suppressing these reactions is not ideal. For example, when you feel yourself about to get outraged, you stamp it down and do your best to seem cool, calm and collected. Even cheerful! This is a wonderful response in a Cuban-themed bar when you've lost your money, and it makes you a very solid-seeming fellow in emergencies. Unfortunately, it does mean that you may fail to stand up for yourself in situations where you really should. You've spent years deliberately eroding your outrage response

---

74 WHY would you not REVIVE your teammate BEFORE trying to take on that sniper, DangerGoblin420? Why!? Your actions *endangered the entire mission, you swine.*

but what if you should be outraged? What if someone is being unreasonable, insulting, even cruel? Years of suppressing your natural reactions will also have an effect on your ability to properly express your emotions to people who really need you to give them that information.

The sad truth is that non-autistic people listen to tone and visual information far more than actual words. So, if you aren't shouting or crying, and you aren't flailing your arms or contorting your face, it doesn't matter if you calmly, blankly state, 'I am absolutely furious about this.' People will never believe you, not completely, until you seem more like you are losing your shit. Sometimes it's crucial to really seem like you are losing your shit, it turns out. It means that, say, your family member, friend or partner will fully understand the extent of how upset you are. There have been occasions where a loved one has really upset me but I haven't socially signalled it correctly. This meant that they were not *as* sorry, *as* careful on subsequent occasions, *as* able to apologise as they would have been if they had truly known how upset I was. This gap between what I felt I was owed and what I was given caused a resentment that sat there and festered until, much later, I was able to sufficiently explain how upset I had been at the time. All of which could have been avoided! But only if I had, in the actual moment of offence, been *less* sociable, *less* well-behaved.

I have only realised this in my thirties and I certainly could have done with understanding it earlier. Is it a paradox to ask someone to suppress their outrage except when they should express it? No, because you are only being asked (by those around you, by society) to lower your level of outrage in situations where it is not seen as appropriate and to keep your outrage for situations where it is. It is not a paradox, it is a tedious demand for you, as an autistic person, to painfully and slowly figure out through trial and error which situation is which, ideally without anyone getting hurt. This is not ideal but this is the reality we are faced with.

It can make you oversimplify situations

It can also lead to what you might call a 'Caesar or nothing' approach to life. This is when you approach life either wanting to be Caesar – the great emperor, the winner, the best – or you are nothing, not involved, a peasant, an 'orrible little worm.

When I was growing up I remember my dad saying to me, on a few occasions, that I was very lucky that I was good at the things that I was interested in. That I was lucky I was often good at the things I enjoyed. Now, clearly there is a chicken and egg aspect to that, as you are more likely to work hard at something you love and more likely to devote significant extra time to it. For example, I always loved art as a subject but realised around the age of eleven or so that I could never manage to draw some decent hands. This irritated me and my desire to draw hands correctly meant that I spent ages looking at hands, drawing hands, doodling cartoon hands holding things from different angles. I had a spare school notebook brimming with *hands*. You know, like any normal, sociable boy. This is a good example of what my dad meant, my enjoyment, my autistic obsessiveness and hyperfocus all lining up to support my studies.

What I learned from being good at the things I liked was

total impatience and intolerance for any gradual progress at all. I was completely 'Caesar or nothing' about everything. If I wasn't the best *instantly* then I was absolute *dogshit* and anyone who said encouraging things was just being nice to a *loser*. Singing, musical instruments, music in all its forms? Sorry! I'm bad at it. I don't understand it, I don't like choir *or* the music on MTV that everyone else likes, so into the bin it goes. Maths, the second it makes demands of me? It's outta there! If I can't understand it immediately, I will panic, freak out, abandon it and be filled with hot, hot shame. Bye-bye! Physical fitness? Same again! Childhood asthma didn't help but the idea of continuing to exercise despite being utterly useless? Unacceptable. Oh, what's that? If I *suffer* every *day*, I will be rewarded with *gradual* gains over a *long* period of time? Nice try! I'm going to wallow in self-loathing instead and coast during rugby games on my sheer size, thank you. I would ignore any and all subjects that didn't slot neatly into my brain. I suppose there is an argument that this is more efficient. If you know (or think) that you're going to be crap at something, why not redirect valuable time and energy towards something you know you'd be good at? A mature instinct when you're an adult and you've had decades to know yourself and your limitations, but unfortunately less appropriate for a moody teenager without that insight yet. You do not want to hand a teenager keys to the 'fuck this, I'm done' car or they will drive away in it and never come back.

I am just lucky, statistically, that the subjects that worked for me were accepted subjects at school. History, English, art, languages and *some* science were things I could plug into my brain and get on with. This is not down to any special effort on

WHY CAN'T I JUST ENJOY THINGS?

my part. I don't mean to say I didn't work hard – I absolutely did – but I enjoyed it, and so I didn't suffer. I often find that people are impressed with things because they presume that in order to get them you had to suffer some unknown agonies, but often the key is that the person just didn't feel those agonies the way you did.

I'm the same with anyone who has ever learned a musical instrument. I found trying to learn the alto saxophone to be an extremely humiliating experience. It was like when humans try to figure out alien technology in science-fiction movies, pawing ineffectually at buttons and sensors far beyond their primitive minds. However, if you enjoy learning it, that feeling wouldn't have hit you, or not as hard, and you'd spend extra time, your own spare time, tootling about with the saxophone, listening to saxophone artists, googling techniques. You had your own version of my mad book of hands.

Black and white thinking leads to unhealthy levels of self-criticism. I still have almost no respect or pride when it comes to my own achievements. I think it's because I was there when they took place, so there's no surprise. Even writing this book I check my word count and see that I've managed another thousand words and joy flickers, for a moment, and then is out, brief candle. 'Not enough! Not finished yet!' I chide myself and immediately start stressing about all the words *unwritten*. It has taken years and years of work to overcome the fear of failure that paralysed me and stopped me from ever beginning something new. If you are a black and white thinker, failure doesn't seem like the first step to getting good, it seems like a sign you will always fail and should give up. Learning to become a professional stand-up has been a massive help with this problem. I was so utterly obsessed with it that I was willing to learn slowly, over years, and ignore the fact that the improvement in my act was sometimes very gradual. It helps that stand-up fills your body with adrenaline and stress hormones and joy hormones, so it's highly addictive, which helped override my desire to give up after setbacks.

This way of thinking doesn't just affect your learning. For example, I would fail to begin the task of cleaning the flat, something small, part of that crucial 'little and often' philosophy of tidying, because it wasn't the *entire* task. I knew that if I hoovered the corridor, I would be annoyed with myself, filled with tension if I didn't also hoover the whole flat, clean the oven, clean out the fridge, scrub down the shower and the sink, mop the kitchenette floor, descale the kettle and on and on and on. That's a useful urge if you get it on a Sunday morning with the whole day ahead of you. It's less useful if it nags at you during your busy periods where you feel the self-loathing of having a dusty carpet but know you only have an hour before the next thing in your schedule.[75] In other words, not enough time for the Caesar-level cleaning, so you opt for nothing, and the problem gets worse.

It might seem that black and white thinking is nothing but downsides that lead to social anxiety, low self-esteem and stress, but there are upsides. In career terms, an inherently strong sense of justice, love of rules, rigidity of approach could make you a very good lawyer, for example, or mathematician or scientist or building inspector. Any job where it is completely

---

75 Or you just never have the energy because you don't conserve energy for important things like cleaning your flat; you spaff all your energy up the wall by socialising with someone who winds you up or doing someone a favour or working too hard at a project that isn't worth it or etc. etc. etc.

irrelevant how many people love your vibe at the after-work voluntary-but-actually-compulsory drinks and all that matters is pure, measurable skill and reliability. The black and white approach could help by simplifying your life, even while it complicates it in other areas.

In terms of the strong sense of justice autistic people often have, that can definitely be a good thing. I don't think it detracts anything from the achievements of, say, Greta Thunberg, to point out that part of what would have motivated her was her profound sense of justice, her sensitivity to injustice, as an autistic person. After all, millions of non-autistic teenagers had the same information that she did and failed to act as she did. She herself has referred to autism as a 'superpower' but 'under certain circumstances' and I think that's fair. This is not a claim to autistic superiority, at least not inherently – we must remember that fairness and justice are contextual ideas. It all depends on perspective. If you are an autistic person and raised by neo-Nazis or ISIS members, your ideas of 'justice' and 'fairness' will also be very strong but perhaps not viewed as warmly as Greta Thunberg's.

I was certainly obsessed with fairness as a child. Autistic people seem to have an extreme opposition to bullying of any kind, especially when young. Obviously very few people are pro bullying, at least openly, and very few bullies really see themselves as such, but if you're like me you'll be obsessively anti-bullying or pro-fairness to the point of seriously inconveniencing yourself.

There's a chicken and egg aspect here: why are autistic people so sensitive to fairness and against bullying? The rigidity of thinking could lead to autistic people simply clearly identifying any behaviour with a sniff of bullying as 'wrong' and that's that. The experience of autistic people who generally grow up marginalised, bullied, excluded and misunderstood could set them against bullies through first-hand experience. The love of rules could lead to a hatred of bullying simply through the dislike of people who ignore rules and the various sensory sensitivities could also play a role. Bullying does, after all, tend to be physically invasive, loud or aurally irritating and disruptive to whatever you're supposed to be doing (your work, for example).

It's probably a combination of all of the above. You might be reading this as a non-autistic person and thinking, 'Well, I was anti-bullying at school, so what?' To that I would counter: were you? If so, how many times did you verbally or physically intervene in an act of bullying, even at risk to yourself? I don't mean to imply you had some duty that you neglected – childhood is hard enough without added vigilante duties. I simply mean to make clear that when autistic people are against something like bullying it is in the most active sense, it is something you are *compelled* to do. Again, this is not a moral fibre thing, or not entirely. The occasion that springs to mind for me was more of an 'I can't stand this' thing in the moment as opposed to the actions of a selfless martyr.

For context, from the second I entered education, I made a habit of obsessively questioning rules I thought were unjust and intervening in bullying or social unfairness. I was repeatedly informed that I was a 'gobby shite' and got into various levels of scrap with the people whose behaviour I found so objectionable. I would often get into trouble, especially because when you are an Enormous Boy it's easy to seem like the troublemaker to a bored/exhausted/distracted teacher. I had no idea where this need came from but I couldn't stop it, or at least I couldn't deny how upset it made me. I *knew* my life would be easier if I didn't do it, if I kept my mouth shut and was more sociable, less incredibly sensitive to even mild exclusion or jokes about myself or others. I *wanted* to not be like this. I just knew it was something I was compelled to do and that unfairness or bullying could make me incredibly angry instantly.

Again, none of this is hugely moral, none of it was an informed stance or choice; it was just reacting to feelings that even I wished I didn't have. I think this disclaimer is necessary to avoid even a hint that I'm claiming to be naturally moral in some marvellous way. I was not – and if someone was made fun of in a way I thought was justified, I was totally fine with it. Believe me – if I could've waved a magic wand and been in the Cool Gang and felt nothing for my fellow dorks, I am sure I would have. I would've leapt on my motorbike and driven the head cheerleader to prom and never looked back. Me and the head cheerleader on my Harley as I yell over the noise of the engine, asking her if she's heard of Warhammer.

On to the incident. I went to a fancy school, the kind that had a Fifth Form Centre, a short corridor with rooms off it where all the kids roughly fourteen to sixteen years old would have their lockers and congregate at break time. There was a small pool table in an alcove filled with lockers and a guy, let's call him Ned, was playing pool. Ned was older than me but we were friendly as we shared quite a few interests and did

Cadets together. He also had what we would have then called Asperger's syndrome but I don't remember anyone ever really comprehending what that meant. I knew it was *something* and I knew it was why Ned had some pretty rigid routines in his life and some pretty niche obsessions. I would never have imagined that we had the same broad condition. Ned was obsessed with listening to the old radio series of *Doctor Who* and the *Hitchhiker's Guide to the Galaxy* on tape, for example, whereas I had formerly been obsessed with old tapes of *The Goon Show*. Completely different, guys! I look back at Ned and how similar we were in hidden ways and laugh at how much more focused I was on the ways in which we were different: how I didn't have a stammer, how I forced myself to become more sociable (made easier by the fact that I had a nicer year) whereas Ned stayed completely true to himself.

Anyway, good old Ned was trying to enjoy a game of pool during breaktime. A sixteen-year-old who we will call Dec took exception to this. Dec was the sort of kid from a comfortable background who did everything he could to give the impression he was not. I didn't know him except by reputation as a generally unpleasant character who was nevertheless a key part of the popular, rumoured-drug-use gang that every school seems to have. My memory is vague but I think he was furious that Ned was playing pool and he wasn't – truly unforgiveable. He tried to use aggression and intimidation to force Ned to hand over the pool cue, to end his game early, but Ned, very calmly, and through his stammer, refused.

Throughout this process, with Dec's increasingly rude and angry demands and Ned's shy attempts to keep the situation calm in spite of Dec, there was a growing atmosphere of tension. I remember having that sick feeling in my stomach you get when you just hope that something won't keep escalating. People were trying not to look at either of them or each other. It would have been impossible to articulate at the time but Dec's behaviour was also, when I think about it as an adult, *embarrassing*. I often wonder if people like that change of their own volition as they grow up or if the context of society around them changes and they are forced to adjust. Do they stop starting fights over pool cues because they grow up and mature, or do they stop because if you try that in a pub as an adult you will get your head kicked in? At the time I was painfully aware that no one would stand up for Ned. Ned didn't have house parties, couldn't get you booze, he liked doing orienteering with me and the other dorks. Dec was socially powerful even without his violent reputation and nasty temper.

Dec did not accept Ned's quiet defiance. He decided to alternate between calling Ned a fucking retard and asking Ned why he was such a fucking retard – a truly Socratic bully. Ned quietly replied that he was not a retard, but Dec seemed to be getting angrier and angrier. I felt ashamed of myself – I liked Ned. Plus, Dec and the rest of his gang just got away with being *like this* all the time. There didn't seem to be any consequences, people didn't even seem to view this behaviour as *dislikeable*! I piped up and I remember I had that awful cold feeling you get when you try to intervene in anything. Here's a blurry recollection of the interaction:

'Dec, why are you such an arsehole all the time?' I asked. Logical, to the point, open to the *idea* of an explanation. Some unhelpful 'ooohs' from observers.

'What the fuck did you say?' Dec wasn't immediately on board with my inquiry.

'Why are you such an arsehole all the time? Just don't be an arsehole.'

This back and forth repeated a bit, but to summarise Dec got very close to me and informed me that if he ever saw me out in town he would 'fucking get me' and 'stab me up'. Dec stormed off, presumably to some sort of lair. Obviously excessive, I thought even at the time, but throughout the rest of that day various people came up to me and asked me if it could *possibly* be true that I had been so incredibly unwise as to say anything to Dec, a well-known, short-fused lunatic? I admit I hadn't been aware of the scale of his reputation – maybe I'd have stayed quiet if I had been – but certainly the notion of being attacked out in town, on the high street, became more real with each excited, horrified interaction during the rest of the day. 'Joke's on him!' I thought – 'I don't *go* into town! I stay at home and play on the computer. Checkmate!' But I was worried.

Reader, he never stabbed me up. He didn't even stab me down. For a while afterwards he would glower at me. It was clear he hated me, emissaries from distant social groups and years above would inform me as much, but no stabbing up. After months of this phoney war I figured that was it, although shortly before he did his GCSEs and left the school for good he did bludgeon me across the face with one of those dense, neon plastic cups schools seem to have. Those ones that have a scratchy, chunky aspect to them like fibreglass. The hard base of the cup opened up a gash on my eyebrow where he caught me. It was a small wound but even a small head wound creates a fabulous amount of blood and the effect was dramatic.

There were lots of little, less gashy incidents than this one throughout my life. People, especially online, like to make lots of noise about how the obsession with rules and fairness and logic in autism is some kind of marvellous benefit. They can sometimes seem like they want autism to be reclassified as Knight of the Realm Disease. While it's certainly true that if everyone was so obsessed with fairness and rules society would be, if not generally better, much calmer and more stable, there are still disadvantages.

Cup-wielding loons aside, I went to a very good school: what if I'd had these impulses at a bad school? I had certainly been in a lot more fights at my less nice primary school, where one of the notoriously naughty kids had to be sent off the island to England because social services couldn't handle him.[76] What if I had these autistic outbursts in the kind of school where people really did mean it when they threatened to stab you? You might say that in those contexts you'd simply adjust your behaviour, but that's the problem – the behaviour is hard to change. It's an instinctive reaction that simply has to be suppressed. I am mature and cynical enough now that I fight the urge to intervene when I see, say, two drunk blokey-looking idiots fighting in the road. I like to think if it was one drunk bloke and one innocent party I'd intervene and, on that note, I did physically intervene the other day when a Deliveroo driver was being shoved off his

---

76 'How naughty can a primary school kid be?' you may ask! I think he pushed a three- or four-year-old kid off a pier and into the sea while the parents were distracted, threw rocks through windows, bit his case worker, these were the tales that reached us. Not exactly Dennis the Menace stuff.

bike and beaten with it by a furious gentleman late at night. It was pointless, unwise and unhelpful. What if they were actually dangerous? The Deliveroo guy didn't care he'd been briefly helped out, the 'gentleman' was furious, the police did nothing and overall it was a net loss for everyone involved. What if the unfair person you are standing up to is part of the system? What if you get these boiling reactions to what you perceive as injustice but the person dishing out the injustice is a bouncer? Or a policeman? Perhaps it is an abstract moral 'superpower' but it's also another way in which autistic people are vulnerable, especially those who are less able to mask or suppress their reactions.

It may also be that an autistic person labels someone as 'bad' in their black and white way but in fact they are not, or they have their reasons for being 'bad'. This rigid approach can be why some people, completely incorrectly, describe autistic people as having less empathy. There's a fuller refutation of that idea in Chapter 7 but let's imagine a simple example. Bob is a bully who bullies smart kids because his parents are cruel to him for getting bad results. Bob bullies an autistic kid, who labels Bob as bad. The autistic kid would more than likely completely forgive or at least understand Bob better if he knew Bob's situation. Bob won't tell the kid because, if Bob can even understand it himself, he is ashamed, maybe afraid. The autistic kid wouldn't imagine any of this because it's not logical: why would Bob feel bad when his parents are the ones being horrible? And if Bob wants to get better results, why would he bully the smart kids instead of asking for help? And if he's afraid, why doesn't he tell a teacher like we are told? Bob's behaviour is technically illogical, but totally understandable once you know all the facts, once you adopt a non-autistic perspective.

I think a non-autistic/neurotypical perspective is one of the most important things I got from obsessively reading fiction and, later, obsessively reading people's online posts about their personal problems. Because autistic people are a tiny minority, we are obliged to comprehend the non-autistic/neurotypical perspective – it does not happen the other way around. I would sit on the internet for *hours* reading about people's issues on self-help forums, for example. It fascinated me and could unlock a new perspective or maybe help me understand a view I wouldn't have otherwise understood. I am aware that I sound like a kindly alien. Unfortunately, every autistic trait you learn to compensate for creates new problems. I became so good at imagining reasons, lovely, valid, emotionally resonant reasons, for people's awful behaviour that I started letting them get away with things I shouldn't. I remember getting very frustrated at one point because I realised I had gone from being socially unusual in taking everything seriously to being socially unusual for taking almost nothing seriously. That might sound like a Zen paradise of the mind, but even in a healthy relationship you need boundaries. It also undermines people's faith in some of your other values or behaviours because now you weren't offended *enough* at something offensive and maybe secretly you approved of it? Oh no! A lot of life for autistic people is this relentless calibration exercise, having to zone in on the sweet spot by going too far or not far enough in ever smaller amounts, like some mad abstract game of hot or cold.

A big part of communication issues between autistic people

WHY CAN'T YOU SEE THAT I AM CORRECT?

and everyone else is that people don't say what they mean, or they only partially express themselves. A great example – who knows if it's true – went viral on Twitter, where an autistic little boy gets permission to stroke a stranger's kitten. The boy and his mother then have to leave, so the mother tells him to 'say thank you', meaning thank the stranger for letting you stroke the kitten that she owns. The boy looks directly at the kitten and says, 'Thank you.' Very polite – why would you not thank the creature you had just been touching? The mother's instruction was ambiguous. To an older child it would've been more obvious, easier to infer the right person to thank, but that's down to socialisation; that doesn't make the mother's statement any less ambiguous.

I like to use the example of the hologram in *I, Robot,* the Will Smith movie, to explain some of my issues with questions. The hologram only has certain information programmed into it, but you only get the hologram to say this information by asking the right question. Every time Will Smith, trying to solve a murder, asks the hologram a very valuable question that it doesn't recognise, it just says, 'I'm sorry, my responses are limited. You must ask the right questions.' Will Smith gets very angry indeed. In this scenario, I am the hologram and Will Smith is any teacher or girlfriend. Let's say I go to see a movie with a friend and on the way there I see a guy dressed as a clown on the train acting weirdly. Later on, if you ask me how the movie was, I will tell you about the movie and probably not mention the clown, because that has nothing to do with the movie and you never asked about the train journey. I am also fully aware that it would be odd for you to ask about the train journey, but hey, that's not my fault. I know this seems like I am being wilfully obtuse and withholding information that anyone would presume was interesting, but I am not!

If you grow up autistic, aware or unaware, you grow up being socially wrong all the time. I spent decades talking *way too much* about things that people actually found boring or at the very least not fascinating. It's embarrassing to realise over and over again that you've been socially burdensome, boring, weird and so on, so you learn to shut up. You behave more like someone under police interrogation, only giving out information that you are *sure* they want, based on their *exact* words. This will lead to an argument with your parents/teachers/partner that you didn't tell them about something *even though they asked*, and, like a hologram, you will have to explain to them that they didn't *actually* ask. They will not like this, but you are technically correct and to be fair, you did save yourself an enormous amount of time, anxiety and energy. It's another example of unlearning or compensating for an autistic trait that creates new issues.

CHAPTER 7

Why Don't I Know
How I Feel?

Until I began the diagnostic process, I had never heard of the word 'alexithymia'. Don't get me wrong, there are plenty of words I've never come across, but I was surprised because (probably as part of being autistic) I was obsessive about words. I'd heard of, I don't know, 'antisyzygy' for example,[77] so I feel justified in thinking of myself as, if not the king of words, certainly a baron of nouns.

I came across the word researching autism before I decided to go for an assessment and it was one of the discoveries that convinced me I was likely to have it. Alexithymia is defined as a difficulty in recognising or identifying one's own emotional

---

77 It refers to the idea of duelling polarities within one entity but is almost always used in the context of 'Caledonian antisyzygy', a term invented by G. Gregory Smith to describe what he saw as the possibly inherent contrary nature of Scottishness, always at war with itself. I once forgot the word and spent an entire afternoon trying to google it without remembering the word at first and then not remembering how it was spelled. It was agony.

state. That's not to say that you don't feel emotions: it's that you experience emotions but have trouble interpreting them, describing them or taking them into consideration.

Alexithymia is a relatively recently defined phenomenon, so our understanding of it is still very basic. I've seen it described as a 'condition' or even simply a 'personality trait'. It used to be seen as a dysfunctional adult personality type but research in developmental neuropsychology found it could be either a problem of cerebral organisation, a marked lack of suitable models during development or both at once. It could also be a condition caused by a chronic response to childhood or adolescent stress. After all, being autistic can be very stressful and cortisol and alexithymia have been linked.[78] It is a condition all on its own, separate from autism, but it does occur *with* autism frequently. I've seen estimates and studies that put the rate of alexithymia among autistic people around 50 per cent and some as high as 85 per cent. Regardless, it's common. It is also common among people with other conditions, such as PTSD. It's also a spectrum because nothing in mental health can ever be simple. So, you can have alexithymia to the pretty mild extent I seem to, or you can have profound alexithymia, with some people reporting that they go through most of their lives not really sure about how they feel about anything and not understanding what other people mean when they describe their own emotions.

78   Goerlich, K.S. and Votinov, M. 'Hormonal abnormalities in alexithymia', *Front Psychiatry*, 9 January 2023 13:1070066. DOI: 10.3389/fpsyt.2022.1070066. PMID: 36699481; PMCID: PMC9868825.
Hua, J., Le Scanff, C., Larue, J., José, F., Martin, J.C., Devillers, L. and Filaire, E. 'Global stress response during a social stress test: impact of alexithymia and its subfactors', *Psychoneurodocrinology*, 5 December 2014; 50:53-61. DOI: 10.1016/j.psyneuen.2014.08.003. Epub 12 August 2014 PMID: 25179321.

WHY DON'T I KNOW HOW I FEEL?

Anyone reading this will be aware that sometimes they catch themselves feeling slightly odd and realise that something has unexpectedly made them feel very slightly, gently sad, or nostalgic. You will realise it after you have already been feeling the feeling for a little while, maybe for a minute, or a morning, and maybe only when you think about your day and solve the mystery of what sparked the feeling. Maybe some familiar smell or the sight of a street where you used to live. With alexithymia, you have that vagueness about how you feel and why even with powerful emotions.

To give an example: if you're afraid of spiders, then seeing a spider in your bath could increase your heart rate, make your breathing change and make your stomach feel weird. However, if you are on a date with someone you are really into and you think they might be about to kiss you then your body will also increase your heart rate, change your breathing and make your stomach feel weird. If you don't have alexithymia, you will easily be able to tell the difference between terror and excitement. If you have alexithymia, you might not be able to tell the difference as easily. Now, that's obviously an overly simple example. From context, it's easy to presume that you aren't in love with a spider you've found in your bath. You are not standing in the bathroom as if you not only caught the spider in the bath but caught them in the bath *naked* and they *aren't telling you to leave, oh my.* I am not claiming that people with alexithymia will flush that spider down the drain while thinking 'wait ... did I want to fuck that spider?'

What I am saying is that someone with alexithymia might instinctively fear intimacy as a result of not being able to interpret these signals correctly. It will be more a case of

'Oh man, when she was getting all intense with me, I felt freaked out, uncomfortable', and, let's be honest, your heart beating through your chest and feeling butterflies in your stomach *is* uncomfortable in the sense that it's a disruption. If your mind interprets it as fear then, well, it's as good as being afraid for real. There is also a fear of rejection or failure in romance, so confusingly there is legitimate fear mixed in there. You will be at risk of deciding that actually this person makes you feel uncomfortable, or afraid, or maybe they're too intense, when in reality you just really like them. And it's not only confusion between excitement and fear, there can be all sorts of problems with alexithymia.

It can be very difficult to tell the difference between sadness and anger, for example. It can also be difficult to tell if you are feeling those things at all. If you are autistic, you can partly blame slow emotional processing for the overall speed but not the lack of instantaneous reaction. For example, plenty of people throughout my life have said offensive things to me or attempted to get a reaction out of me, but unless I am really on edge due to other factors (fatigue, physical danger), I will rarely react. Frankly, I rarely feel the anger I am supposed to when someone is rude and the autistic part of me sometimes even appreciates the clear communication. Someone could say something provocative and I would feel more irritated if I didn't understand *why* they were being rude, or why they'd bother. If it was someone I already knew had a huge problem with me, well, that's expected behaviour from them and what else is there to say? This can cause difficulties by implying to someone who wishes you ill that you have no boundaries or maybe that they can go even further than they thought in provoking you. There are some people who will get even angrier with you if they fail to provoke a reaction and so they will escalate their behaviour to get what they want – maybe they'll move from verbal insults to physical violence, for example.

When I was at primary school, I was far more reactive and would lose my temper when provoked quite easily as I erred on the side of 'I am unsure how I feel about that, but I know it was bad. Better react strongly, just in case.' These days, I do the inverse. Someone could insult my mother in a pub and mistake my utterly neutral response as a sign of the deep calm of the trained assassin. My vaguely alexithymic reactions were a social burden in childhood and are a benefit in adulthood. It's not down to some sort of personal growth I have achieved this ability so much as a simple change of contextual rules. School didn't have bouncers, after all. Context is everything. I think if someone drew ejaculating penises all over their desk in an *office environment*, our collective assumption would be that the perpetrator needed psychiatric help.

There can also be issues in less confrontational situations. Let's say that your partner does or says something that is upsetting to you. Any situation in which a normal person would respond with pretty instant anger or irritation. For example, I was once having lunch with a partner and felt I was expressing some deep vulnerability or insight about myself. They responded fairly indelicately and indicated that they were deeply bored with the conversation and wished to change the subject. In the moment, a neurotypical person would have been angry or at the very least reacted in a way that broadcast 'I feel negatively about what you have said.'

In the moment, I definitely felt something. I wasn't shocked – I'm autistic, I have often spoken for far too long in far too much detail about topics. I have worked very hard to try and limit that and, if I fail, I try not to be too hurt by someone not being as fascinated with the early medieval Gaelic kingdom of Dál Riata as I am. I would say I felt a little blow in the stomach area and an awareness that I needed to process what was said as quickly and as diplomatically as possible, to try and rapidly figure out what I should do or what was correct. I maintained a neutral expression and said something vague and accommodating like 'Oh, OK, sure.' Over the next few minutes I was externally placid but internally feverishly trying to decipher how I felt. I definitely felt negative. Sad? Definitely sad that I was clearly being boring. Was this the normal feeling of vague regret and embarrassment that I felt when I spoke for too long about a special interest topic? It was similarly shameful.

But then I tried to judge it like a lawyer in my own mind. I took the topic I was discussing, a personal vulnerability, and decided that it was definitely not the same as a special interest topic. It was different to discuss something intimate and vulnerable, for example, than to spend five minutes trying to get someone to understand, really understand, that in the early medieval British Isles travel by sea was far more efficient than by land. Slowly, I started to think, 'hang on, there's a chance I should be annoyed here! Should I be annoyed?' Oh God, by now it was minutes later, it was too late to react with anger. You'd look like a fucking cartoon henchman, some sort of easily tricked meathead! Like some character who gets rings run around them by Bugs Bunny,

WHY DON'T I KNOW HOW I FEEL?

'Duuuuh, waaaaait a minute, you'se was bein' rude ta me!' This gets worse the longer you leave it.

Not only that, but what if you're wrong? You've been wrong for so much of your life about rudeness, for example. It turns out it's not rude if your mate makes fun of your clothes – it can be fun banter. It's also not polite to shake someone's hand if they expect a hug, even though a hug is invasive and presumptuous, so who the fuck knows? In this situation, I was intimidated by the idea of expressing my anger. It wasn't only that I was unsure and it felt like a gamble, but also I was aware that I couldn't unexpress it. Plus, after I expressed it, I had no idea what to do next. What if they just said I was wrong to be annoyed? Do I say, 'No, I am not wrong' and then run away? Leap through a manhole cover and into a sewer, start a new life as a superhero down there? 'Justifiably Upset Man'?

There is an argument that part of alexithymia, especially in autism, is induced in someone. Let's say that you are autistic and you find that the feeling of a scratchy jumper you wear for school makes you feel sick. You will naturally complain to your parents or teachers that wearing your jumper makes you feel sick, maybe in an unreasonably loud way, and they will inform you that either: you are wrong and it doesn't do that, or that it doesn't matter and you have to do it anyway 'just like everyone else'. The authority figures in your life, the ones in charge of telling you what is true and what is not, what is important and what is not, are telling you that you are wrong about your own feelings, that you are wrong about what you want. They are also implying that there's a chance everyone feels sick in their jumpers all the time and they don't complain.

If we imagine this happening to an autistic child multiple times a day, most days for their entire lives, is it so unreasonable to stop trusting your gut? To go from thinking, 'Well, maybe it doesn't matter that this jumper makes me nauseous, and if that doesn't matter, why would it matter if anything makes me uncomfortable? Being uncomfortable is clearly what life is all about' or 'Maybe I was being oversensitive about that joke, so maybe it's OK if this friend of mine calls me rude names in front of people.' People throw the term gaslighting around without using it properly but it's undeniable a large part of growing up autistic is being told to doubt your perceptions of the world, sometimes reasonably and sometimes not. The trouble is it can take such a long time to figure out the difference.

Anyway, back to the situation. We sat with our coffees in the awkwardness and slowly moved on to other things but, in the background, I was slowly realising firstly that I was actually pretty angry and secondly that I had missed my chance to do anything about it. I felt this was my fault and chalked the whole thing up to experience, but it never left me. The unexpressed anger fermented into resentment and the whole thing exploded months and months later during a semi-related argument.

Delays in processing

The problem with alexithymia is that in a relationship it can completely suffocate communication like this and your non-autistic partner will have a hard time even accepting you were upset if they go by normal impressions. If you have autism or think you might have it, you may have experienced something similar where it just took you longer to figure out if you were angered, worried or delighted by something. Autism can mean that you have delays in processing information of certain kinds and it can give people the wrong impression or create an awkward situation where you are socially obliged to state your reaction to something earlier than you would like. There's nothing worse than feeling obliged to say, 'No worries' to something only to actually realise that you're annoyed about it three days later. This is because you didn't find yourself to be instantly upset and couldn't quickly think of a good reason to say no, or felt it best to just agree to avoid an awkward pause. Not only that, but suddenly realising it or bringing it up a few days later makes you seem like you've been boiling with fury and hiding it, because you didn't seem instantly upset to the other person and haven't mentioned anything about it since. It's more like the emotions were downloading or delayed in the post. My emotions are delivered by Evri, put it that way.

I've got something weird going on where I won't feel much excitement or adrenaline until the last minute. There are some comedians who talk about feeling sick about a big gig the moment they wake up on the day of it, or maybe even days in advance. With a few exceptions I don't feel nerves, excitement or any adrenaline for 99 per cent of gigs until maybe when arriving at the venue. Then I'll feel a bit like I'm in the cinema watching the trailers for a movie. If I'm doing a comedy club, the adrenaline will only finally hit when the host of the evening goes out to talk to the crowd for a few minutes and then introduces me. If I'm on tour, it'll be when I see the lights go down and get the signal to introduce myself on the offstage mic. Then I get a kind of rollercoaster build-up of excitement, terror, a desire to get out there and do well, an awareness of the possibility of being embarrassed, everything anyone associates with public speaking, all rolled into one big internal Catherine wheel spraying sparks all over the place.

The second I step out onstage, most of the time it goes away again. It's like this big firework display has suddenly had the sound muted and everything slows down and I can finally concentrate and everything will be fine. Some sports professionals describe something like this as a state of flow and I believe, completely anecdotally here in my armchair like the unqualified clown that I am, that the alexithymia or lack of excitement and anxiety leading up to the gig may help me attain a state of flow.

The downside of this is that I do not get excited for things like holidays either, not until I'm on the plane maybe. It always infuriated me growing up how people would ask, 'Are you excited for your holiday?' like we were collectively in some brightly coloured children's television programme. As though I was going to reply, 'Oh YES! H is for Holiday!' before turning to a camera and asking the viewer if they could spell 'holiday'. My most common response to that question is still obviously 'Yes', but I'll be honest, I don't sell it. People are worried by the flatness of my 'Yes'. If you're a particularly kindly old lady, I'll really go for the full masking 'Oooh yes!', big smile and nod and so on. Partially out of politeness but also because I recognise situations where the person is basically asking, 'I think you should feel good, I'd feel good if I were you, and I like you, so I wish for you to feel good. Do you? Oh please say you do!' And I would like them to feel good about me feeling good, so I just say it.

WHY DON'T I KNOW HOW I FEEL?

In situations where I feel able to be honest, I can say, 'I don't know', which is my way of saying, 'Mr Excitement is not currently at home, he may be back later, but I couldn't say when.' Another option is to go balls-out and say, 'No, I have too much to do before then.' I feel like it's difficult to get excited about something when there are other tasks in the way. If I was painting a picture and only just at the stage of buying paint and paintbrushes, you'd be insane, maybe even mocking, to ask me if I was 'excited to sell my painting to someone', wouldn't you? It would seem excessive and getting ahead of yourself. Well, that's me with almost anything. Even the act of getting to the airport and getting through security and onto the plane is a big enough job that I do not feel like I can really afford to look beyond it and get excited until it is done.

Sometimes, especially when I was younger, I would mistake excitement for anxiety when it came to social situations. I remember, years ago, sitting on the Underground on the way to a friend's house party and feeling like I was going to have a panic attack: high heart rate, adrenaline, huge sense of anticipation. By then I had had enough therapy to allow myself to feel the emotion but step back and realise that I was on my way to a house party where there would be only my closest friends. There couldn't be a less stressful situation ahead of me. Often in my life I will list upcoming things that are fun in the same way, with the same energy, as upcoming exams. I'll put my head in my hands before realising that I am being incredibly unreasonable, that I genuinely thought something like, 'Oh *great*, now I have to have *lunch* with one of my *best friends*! Fuck's sake!'

I think a part of my crossed wires is alexithymia, though

with autism it's such a *holistic* bloody thing it's impossible to differentiate between alexithymia making me confused between excitement and stress, actual stress because I would have to socially mask or put lots of energy into socialising, creeping autistic burnout from masking and functioning, and maybe some reaction to the change in routine; the house party meaning that I couldn't eat or drink the stuff I'd planned or expected and so on.

I hope that autistic people, despite not being able to change their level of emotional processing or alexithymia, could use their awareness of these problems to better manage themselves or their expectations and be more confident in saying, for example, 'I don't know how I feel yet, I will need more time.' Maybe non-autistic people, having gained some insight into these challenges, could free up some more space for compassion or patience, or at least reduce the need to assign blame. After all, it's not as though everyone isn't generally trying their best in life. Sometimes it does feel like I am listening to my own mind and body through a wall in the flat next door, glass up to my ear, straining to figure out what the hell my neighbour could be yelling about *this* time.

Interoception

There is growing evidence that issues with interoception are a part of autism.[79] Interoception is basically your sense of what

79 Williams, Z.J., Suzman, E., Bordman, S.L., Markfeld, J.E., Kaiser, S.M., Dunham, K.A., Zoltowski, A.R., Failla, M.D., Cascio, C.J. and Woynaroski, T.G. (2023). 'Characterizing Interoceptive Differences in Autism: A Systematic Review and Meta-analysis of Case-control Studies. J Autism Dev Disord.' Mar; 53(3):947-962. DOI: 10.1007/s10803-022-05656-2. Epub 2022 11 July PMID: 35819587; PMCID: PMC9832174

is happening inside your body. It's your ability to sense your heart rate, temperature, breathing, if you're hungry, need the toilet and so on. You'd think that these senses are so inherent that you can't really exist without them, but that's not quite the case. You only drink because you feel thirsty – let's imagine that during a busy day you simply never felt thirsty. Can you honestly say you'd drink as much water? Some of the best advice I ever got was from a very intense American lady who insisted that the first thing one should do in the morning is immediately drink a big glass of water. I think she meant it more for skin complexion reasons but it's great advice for me specifically. I can honestly say that, growing up, I would almost never drink anything. The sheer, literally unquenchable lust that Americans have for hydrating seems insane to me, but after that lady's advice I tried out drinking a more reasonable number of glasses of water as a matter of routine, whether I was thirsty or not, and I can honestly say I felt better, less tired and less hungry. Part of me not drinking enough during the day could be down to hyperfocus, it's true, but that doesn't explain why I didn't drink any water even on days when I was farting around.

I also never quite feel full. I remember reading once that some Labradors have a specific gene that makes it harder for them to feel full and satisfied. I felt very seen. Yet another similarity between me and dogs.[80] A few times in my life, due to boredom and compulsion, I have eaten and eaten and eaten until I finally feel full to the extent I can *feel* that food isn't fitting in my *stomach* anymore. Horrible feeling, but how else

---

80 Needing many hours of sleep, thrive with a routine, love of meat.

do people know? Often I am also mistaking thirst for hunger. It is a little embarrassing to wish that I had an automated food dispenser fitted with a timer, like a cat, but it would solve a lot of problems. For now, though, when I am functioning well, I use a food tracker app. I know that a lot of people have issues with tracking food and I understand, but without the app I can literally eat more than double the calories I need in a day by *accident* without realising and it drives me up the wall. So, it's a case of choosing the lesser of two evils. There does appear to be a link between alexithymia and OCD, body image disorder and serious binge eating.[81]

Interoception and alexithymia together can cause issues when it comes to exercise. If you don't get good enough signals from your body, you can miss some important stuff. Once, on a long train journey, I was faced once again with cramming my mighty frame into a tiny plastic seat. To alleviate the discomfort I sat at forty-five degrees, since the seat next to me was empty, like I wanted the ticket inspector to see me and think, 'Gosh, look how casual this guy is – *someone's* taken the train before!' Anyway, I had my right foot up on my left knee for the entire journey and, in layman's terms, completely fucked it. It was months before my knee was right again and it was agony almost immediately after standing up. It had felt a little weird during the train journey but why not immediately?

I get this a lot with knees, my back, shoulders and joints generally. When I'm training at the gym with an instructor and they ask me if I can feel this or that sensation in my body, I often answer with 'I don't know.' I find it so difficult to tell

---

81 https://www.frontiersin.org/journals/psychiatry/articles/10.3389/fpsyt.2019.01026/full

firstly, what they even mean and secondly, if I am feeling the thing that they say I should be. I've had people say, 'OK, and could you feel that in your lower back?' and I frown and think, 'Well, I mean, a bit, but maybe that was because I can feel my lower back in general? Wait, which bit of my lower back?' It takes me a good few seconds to even figure out which muscles are being tensed or engaged in a particular exercise. I've been doing a lot of weightlifting in the past few years and it has helped a lot. Without weightlifting, I would have an even worse awareness of my body and how it all fits together and doing it with a trainer sometimes, or a more experienced person, is great because I cannot tell you how many exercises I've been doing over the years with completely the wrong muscles. I haven't been kicking medicine balls around the gym and muttering about how I can't wait to have biceps, but not far off it.

Autism is also commonly co-occuring with hypermobility and Ehlers-Danlos syndrome, a condition that affects your connective tissues. They are different conditions and there are lots of different kinds of EDS but they do seem to co-occur quite consistently. Potential slogan: 'Obsessed with trains? Then there's a good chance you're floppy!' Isn't that catchy? Before you yoga nuts get jealous, it's not floppy in a good way. It's floppy in a 'that really shouldn't bend that way' sort of way and it leaves you open to a lot of injuries and early joint problems.

At the time of writing I don't have a diagnosis of EDS and I'm not sure how to get one or what it would be for, since there's no cure or anything. I'm definitely hypermobile, though. It turns out that very few enormously heavy, six-foot-four men can sit on their ankles indefinitely or press their palms together in prayer in between their own shoulder blades without trying. I used to live above a Bikram yoga studio and get discounted classes. I'd go every now and then as way of simultaneously doing and avoiding exercise. I once told a female friend that I'd been going to Bikram yoga classes and she reacted as though I'd told her I'd been going to Vagina School and learning to love my breasts. She's an intensely progressive person and I think her hysterical laughter really let the side down that day. In fairness to her, the only other men who were ever in the class were either insanely shredded Instagram models who look like their job on a census form would be 'Spiritual Fuckboy' or skinny, white hippies with dreadlocks and dreamcatcher tattoos. Very few hairy, pale men without a proper mat wearing old rugby shorts and with my body type (village executioner). I'd tell myself that it was the same as doing cardio and weights because my heart rate was up and I was sweating. I don't know how true that is, I imagine that's not how it works. If it did, people would just bend over repeatedly in a big oven and lose loads of weight. I can't think of any real-world activity that mimics what happens in Bikram yoga – the closest thing is probably bending down to scavenge cigarette butts off the pavement in Dubai in summer. Anyway, I was a teacher's pet because I would show up after weeks of no practise, no pre-stretching and nail it. Occasionally I would even earn praise from the extremely camp man/Zen older woman/thin-but-eerily-strong lady running the class, so it's not all bad. Sure, if I do a marathon, my knees will explode, but hey, I don't want to do a marathon.

For all these reasons I only realised as an adult that the

pain I associated with exercise was also just ... exercise. Not all the time: sometimes it was muscular pain and sometimes it was simply sheer lack of fitness, but often it was just due to exercise. Everyone always said that if an exercise hurts you should stop for safety, but if it all hurt or felt like it might be hurting, then what does one do? It didn't help that I was very asthmatic as a kid.

I remember once doing cross country and (with hindsight) finding it hard to differentiate between the normal agony in my lungs and legs and the bad kind of agony. My PE teacher told me to pick up the pace, reasoning with me that 'the sooner you finish cross country, the more time you'll have to rest'. Not the time to get into a logic battle with an autist, I would say. I rasped out, 'The faster ... I run ... the more time ... I'll need ... to rest?' I was also baffled by the suggestion that cross country was something I was wandering through, like I knowingly had more in the tank but simply didn't feel like giving it my all. Did this man not understand that, as we spoke, I was inside my personal hell? Did he have no idea that reality had shrunk down to a never-ending rural pavement and the incomprehensible swirl of pain signals from my body? Interrupted only by a great pang of humiliation as yet another white-clad child glided past me as if pulled along by invisible string?

Looking back, the PE teacher was trying to get me to tolerate more of the normal agony of exercise so I could get fitter, but I had no idea how to tell the difference back then and his logical rhetoric left me cold. Maybe if he had said, 'The sooner you finish, the more time you'll have to rest. This is based on the fact that the amount of rest you will need from any level of exertion increases in relation to the level of exertion at first, but eventually that curve flattens. For example, you will never need to spend more than ten minutes resting to get your breath back.' And maybe followed by some helpful graphs and various studies? It's a lot to ask from a teacher mid-run, to be fair, I can see that now.

It's also an issue when speaking to doctors or nurses. No one can ever truly measure or know another person's physical pain, of course. We have all struggled to articulate our pain level with that idiotic scale of 1–10, occasionally accompanied by little drawings of faces. Level 1 pain tends to have a face that looks like the expression you'd pull if you were swimming in the sea and came across a patch of inexplicably warm water and level 10 will have a sort of weeping face where the caption should be something like 'a-boo-hoo-hoo!', which seems inappropriate for the *highest level of human pain*. I suppose if your eyes are rolling into the back of your head and you're throwing up, they can't show you the ten smiley faces anyway.

There have been many times in my life where I have struggled to describe the pain I am feeling or its type. Well-meaning professionals will ask me if it is a stabbing pain or a dull ache and you have to believe me when I say I do my best to tell them. Sometimes it's easy, sometimes it's like being asked if you just saw a crow or a raven fly by the window. Autistic people will have worse outcomes when it comes to exercise, diet and health thanks to these difficulties, so it's a bit of a raw deal and all we can hope for is that more people are made aware of the risks so it can be managed.

CHAPTER 8

Why do People Think
I am Rude?

A lot of autistic people, especially undiagnosed ones, are considered blunt or rude by non-autistic people. Part of this may be due to sensory issues or executive function issues. For example, if there is a noise or smell that is making you feel physically sick or in pain, you probably won't come across as the cheeriest conversation partner, or if you struggle with multitasking, you'll miss social cues like the little face dance someone does when they have an anecdote to tell that relates to the current topic of conversation. That little happy, hopeful face where they open their mouth a little, ready to speak, and raise their head: Anecdote Face. It's a signal that not only did they *also* go to Portugal on holiday but they *also* had the same weird local booze. You might miss that and go blundering on to a new topic of conversation, ruining their hopes of anecdote delivery and forcing them to re-set to 'listening face'. Unforgiveable! But there are other reasons, more related to the literal way autistic people approach the world, that could give us a bad social reputation among the non-autistics.

For example, it took me years of pub-style conversations to understand that, when someone poses a question, they rarely want it answered. If everyone is sitting around and hanging out, chatting idly, the person who poses a question is not primarily after answers. What they are doing is chucking a conversational football into the middle of the group. They are saying, 'Hey guys, since we've kicked away that last conversational football, how about now we kick this one around? I think it'll be pretty fun to kick and it'll soak up some time.'

When you leap in like Autism Man, weighted cape flapping, and swiftly answer the question with something awful like a fact, or even antisocially look up the answer on your phone, you are essentially picking up the football they have thrown into the circle and bursting it with a knife. Questions and thoughts are merely conversation cud for us to slowly chew like cattle with no particular purpose or destination. Once I figured that out, I could mostly go along with it, because now I understood the *purpose* of the questions and if I didn't know the answer I could stop myself from immediately looking it up (my natural instinct) and sincerely participate. A good rule of thumb is that neurotypical people almost never mean what they say and are often trying to accomplish some mysterious third goal.

Another way you can screw up as an autistic person is by telling the truth. When you are very young, you are told repeatedly by various authority figures (parents, God, brightly coloured puppets) that lying is bad and telling the truth is good.

WHY DO PEOPLE THINK I AM RUDE?

People will throw around phrases like 'You should always tell the truth'. Obviously, it is good to make sure that children are honest when they are young and vulnerable because it means they are easier to care for. However, if you tell people the truth as an adult, hoo boy, you are going to be in trouble a lot. I think my fellow autistics would have appreciated a big meeting around the age of twelve where our parents, God and the puppets got us into a huddle and said, 'OK, here's the thing guys, good job telling the truth about emergencies or crime, but aside from them it's time to lie almost constantly.'

I've tried to speak to non-autistic people about this but it doesn't work, mainly because we do not agree on what a lie is. If you are feeling awful and someone says, 'How are you?' and you say, 'Fine,' you would probably classify that as politeness. I would classify that as a lie. It's an untrue statement delivered with full awareness of its untrueness: it's a lie. The *intent* of the lie is polite, I agree with you there, and it doesn't make the teller of the lie a bad person, but intent doesn't make a lie true. When I say I classify 'fine' as a lie, I don't just mean semantically, as part of some pedantic little exercise. Like some smirking teenager throwing tomato into a fruit salad and pretending he doesn't see the problem since it's all *fruit actually, MUM*. No, when I say that I classify 'fine' as a lie, I mean it with my whole chest. It *feels* like lying to me, like I am telling a lie. It feels like it takes far more energy than telling the truth; it feels a little stressful, like pretending to have seen a film.

It feels stressful in the same way it feels stressful when your friend asks you for advice or for your input and you know *exactly* how to help them but it would hurt their feelings. You're buddies with Smelly Bill and he can't understand why people don't sit next to him. You *know* the reason, you could solve all of his problems at once, but you lie anyway, say you don't know, and thus condemn your friend to misery. Ironically, if you are autistic, you are more likely to blurt out, 'You SMELL, Bill, people think you SMELL' to his face. You learn the hard way that this can end badly. Then again, a few times in my life, I have experienced the thrill of genuinely being able to help someone through telling them something that no one else would. It's a hell of a high, but a risky one.

It can feel depressing if I'm lying in this way to someone I know well. I'll think, 'I'm lying to my friend about how I am! How depressing, isn't the point of having a friend that I shouldn't have to do this? I wouldn't want *them* to lie!' It can also create resentment in me if I am lying to a stranger or someone I know less well to put them at ease, like *they* are making me lie. They have asked me a question that they must *know* I am socially forbidden to answer honestly. I resent it also because why bother even asking if you know what I am going to say? What pointless ritual is this? That means that when you say, 'How are you?' you aren't even really asking how I am, and when I say, 'Fine' back, I am not really telling you! This is an *insane* waste of energy!

I have recently started answering honestly. Not all the time, I'm not totally nuts. If I sit next to a stranger at a wedding I will say, 'Fine' in all the right places and do my best not to mention how much I've been reading about different historical alphabets or my broken boiler. However, in more mundane situations, I'll answer honestly and watch for the person's reaction. You will learn something very valuable: the extent to which that person actually wants to know how you are. This has probably upped the rate of people who have thought of me as rude or boring. When I was younger, I thought of this as insincere well-wishers getting what they deserved. Now that I am older, I can say to my fellow autistics that these poor non-autistics are just as trapped by scripts as we are. I say this because, if I am honest and mention my broken boiler, the non-autistic person is obliged to display sympathy and ask further questions about something as dull as a stranger's knackered old boiler. They often don't like us answering them honestly because they see it as us *obliging them* into *our* sick little game. If we'd said, 'Fine' then both parties could move on to a further subject more likely to be of mutual significance.

Fair enough, non-autistics. I just wish we could be more honest about the role of these silly rituals. People seem reluctant to admit that they are often 'dangerous person filtering systems' and not sincere conversation. Someone meeting a stranger is essentially saying, 'Hello – are you sane and calm enough to answer these ritual questions without issue? Or are you *so mad* that your thoughts cannot be contained?' It's like the vague mental health version of asking a concussed person who the prime minister is. An autistic person's answers will strike a non-autistic person as dangerously uninhibited, a sign of some mental illness, drug or alcohol use and so on. It's not, of course. It's just boring old autism-flavoured lack of inhibition.

In terms of social bafflement, looking back there were some pretty serious flirting moments that completely passed me by. Not being able to flirt, understand flirting or even notice flirting definitely contributed to my slower social development – especially as guys were expected to take the lead. Fat chance! Could I get off with someone during high school by asking them if *they* were also interested in Japanese woodworking? I was lucky that my first girlfriend, somehow attained during university, was amused by my sketchbook of horribly vivid cartoons on that first ever coffee date we went on. One of them was a cartoon advertising a fictional reality show called *Victorians Without Skin*.

God knows how many people I have offended by either not noticing their flirting, misunderstanding it or rejecting it in panic like someone accidentally picking up a hot oven tray and hurling it, screaming, into the sink. I try not to think about it because it makes me want to live in the woods. If you're going to lie awake at night sweating over something it should be something where you can make a difference.

There's a lot of talk about 'communication styles', but I don't know if there will ever be a way to reconcile the autistic and neurotypical approach to small talk. Either every single non-autistic person needs to adjust their inherited, taught, hundreds-of-years-old idea of small talk that is correct in the vast majority of situations or, more likely, autistic people will have to keep playing the game and masking to some extent. The goal is to see how far we can reduce those expectations on us across society but more realistically in our own lives. For example, you can work in a field like comedy where you are surrounded by other weirdos who have become allergic to small talk and will generally indulge your oddness if you indulge theirs.

Scripts

Something that autistic people have to do to survive non-autistic communication is learn scripts. We don't come to small talk naturally and so instead we may learn scripts, like we are in a never-ending play where everyone is very polite. The role of small talk is social bonding, the words themselves are often meaningless, or divorced from their literal meaning. So, we learn that the answer to 'How are you?' in the script is 'Fine, thanks, how are you?', we learn that the script says the answer to 'Excited for your holidays?' is 'Ooh, yeah, it'll be good to get away' or something about the weather, and so on. So many conversations that happen during the day are basically telemarketing – stick to the script!

One of the problems with learning hundreds and hundreds of scripts throughout your life is that you can start to get very good at predicting where conversations will go. I know an autistic person who finds this incredibly relaxing. They see small talk as an Official Way To Speak To People that saves them the time and agony of figuring out what people want in every single tiny chat. It saves them a huge amount of energy by reducing the need for masking and the stress and anxiety of getting things wrong, especially in a work setting. I found this fascinating because I am completely the opposite. Once again, it seems autism is about coming at something from either too far to one side or too far to the other.

I find the prevalence of social scripts and small talk absolutely exhausting. I can do it, in the same way that I could speak a second language, but it can be as tiring. I am fluent in neurotypical, to the point that people are often surprised to find out I am not a native speaker, but it is not the language I think or dream in and I am always scrabbling for vocabulary. This might help explain to any neurotypical readers why so much of the autistic conversation is about being tired all the time – it's about the energy you expend having *every single conversation* during the day consciously instead of unconsciously, like if you had to have it in French.

The constant learning of scripts can be a double-edged sword. Autistic people tend to excel at pattern recognition – the brain regions associated with pattern recognition light up more in autistic people than the general population, for example. If you combine the constant, obsessive learning of social scripts with high pattern recognition, you get very good indeed at predicting what people are going to say. I can often predict what they are going to say in real life, on television or in films word for word, though it is easier with television or film since they are literally scripted. When I was younger, I would interrupt people a lot to finish their sentences for them, which some people find very rude and others charitably seemed to see as a sign that I had really 'got' them. However, it's a risk and if the person feels like they have an emotional need to say all their words themselves then they will hate it, and it makes you look like a total arsehole if you interrupt them predictively and get it wrong.

If you combine this predictive ability with a low tolerance for boredom it can ruin social situations and make you look like a prize fuckhead. It turns some conversations into an episode of a sitcom you have already watched hundreds of times but are being forced to pretend is brand new. If I have energy I can manage it but some days it is beyond me. On one of these days

WHY DO PEOPLE THINK I AM RUDE?

I was sitting in a restaurant with three companions and the conversation turned to vaping. A complicating factor of this prediction problem is that, as a comedian and writer as well as an autistic person, I can spend the whole day reading articles and absorbing opinions. This means I have already read all the various opinions on vaping that exist as well as the ones I have heard in conversation. I have seen all the memes. I am happy to admit that is entirely my problem and no one else's fault. I was already in a unique situation with the autism and that has been compounded by my line of work, obsessive reading and internet usage. I don't want to seem like I am 'above' the conversations that I can predict, my brain has simply put me in an unusual position that I do not enjoy and cannot change. I am more than aware that if I changed the subject of the group's conversation to one I preferred, say the Habsburgs, *they* would feel trapped and bored.

When the subject of vaping came up I was a little bored but mainly filled with dread because I sensed what was coming. It's a big scripted conversation and I know I don't have the energy for it. The conversation covers the bases I thought it would: vaping is likely better than smoking although we don't know enough yet to be sure; vaping can help you quit smoking, but some people (often Gen Z) just start vaping without ever smoking first, which seems crazy especially to us (millennials); kids also vape and this is bad and there are some stories in the press about kids getting lung problems, but it's not surprising when the vape flavours are so childish and sweet and marketed like energy drinks; disposable vapes are bad for the environment. It was like I saw all of these statements laid out in front of me like musical instruments on a table and I knew that it was my job to pick one to say in advance, to choose which instrument I would play in this little song about vaping.

I couldn't do it. It felt so incredibly, agonisingly fake. I was desperate to 'break character' and ask everyone else if they could see it the way I did. I was desperate to know if they were also picking obvious things to say in advance or did they feel like the statements were as spontaneous as real opinions? How did they cope with saying things they didn't really mean or have any interest in when they *could* be saying things they *did* mean that *were* interesting to them? If they had no idea what I meant, I wanted to ask them if they had really, truly never heard any of the things they were saying before. They must have heard it before because whenever someone said a new thing about vaping everyone would *nod.* Was the whole thing a way of proving that we had all heard the same things? Was it reassuring to know that we were all on the same page? I could never actually ask them any of this. Mainly because it would seem rude and inexplicable. The deeper reason I would never ask them something like this is because I feared the answer. If they had no idea what I meant, that would confirm my fears that I was completely alone in thinking like this. Not in the world, of course, but in this situation. Unable to explain myself, an incompetent traveller blundering through a foreign land.

I am sure the conversation was entirely normal but to me, people spoke like they were underwater. I was conscious that I wasn't saying much but I couldn't risk speaking. I had already gone to the toilet just before this conversation began, so I couldn't go for a small holiday in the toilet to recharge. I wanted to take the olives from the little bowl on the table and slowly push them under my eyelids. I wanted to say, 'This is taking too long!' and slowly lower my forehead into my starter and stay there until the restaurant had shut. I know this level of intolerance sounds insane and makes me seem a shit, but go online and you will see I am not alone.

An autistic friend of mine agrees with this sentiment and said that on a recent car journey he was trapped in a conversation like this and he wanted to open the door and roll out onto the highway. You have to remember that this happens to autistic people every day forever and normally all is well. It's just that sometimes you've got nothing left in the tank and something hits you in exactly the wrong way and, before you know it, you've got bulging eyelids packed with olives and are mumbling questions about bonding rituals.

It's like being trapped in *Groundhog Day*, being forced to repeat the same conversations in an endless loop despite knowing exactly what's going to happen. Bill Murray's advantage, and his relief, in *Groundhog Day* was the fact that he could flip out, tell these people to shut up, set the building on fire, whatever, safe in the knowledge that it would all be erased when he woke up the next morning and began the same day again. Autistic *Groundhog Day* is worse. You suffer the same agonies but if you flip out, say the wrong thing or offend someone, *everyone remembers.* You get the boredom of repetition but without any consequence-free cathartic release and no restarts. All the looping conversations *plus* the ageing process.

The upside of this accursed power is that it's super-useful in comedy. If you develop an almost algorithmic understanding of language, culture, humour, sentence structure and so on it makes writing jokes and scripts much easier. If I know where a conversation with an audience member is going, then I can go on autopilot and start thinking of something funny to say based on the predicted ending of the upcoming sentence. I can take my own sentences and make them deliberately seem predictable but swap the ending out for an unexpected one that makes people laugh. It's definitely one of the reasons that I wanted to work in comedy – the pursuit of endless novelty! I was determined to never be boring in conversation and never *be* bored in conversation. Or, at the very least, to always be surprised by what someone was saying, to be unable to predict it.

Novelty and surprise doesn't have to be *nice*, by the way. In fact, I have often been (with hindsight) far too tolerant of rudeness or behaviour that crossed certain boundaries simply out of gratitude for the variation it provided. It's definitely a big part of why I place such a premium on humour. To be blunt, I do not want to spend time having conversations I could have simply imagined in my head. As described, if I am too tired, stressed, hungover, whatever, they will make me feel *more* isolated and insane than having no conversation at all.

I am fully aware that this sense of crippling boredom is precisely what a non-autistic person would experience when, say, I ramble on to them about Stalingrad or whatever. Autistic or not, we can't really help what gets to us, it's important to remember that and try to be kind to one another. Other than that general platitude, I can't think of a solution to what we might call Vape Scenarios. I suppose it's up to us to try to minimise the occurrence of the situations but it would be nice to sometimes get some understanding and feel less isolated. The trouble is that it's impossible for people not to take the boredom and hatred of small talk personally, as opposed to simply a sign of different brain wiring, so I am not optimistic. All the autistic self-advocacy in the world will never win us the right to stand bolt upright during a meal and bellow, 'Enough!' before sprinting home.

Double empathy

One of the long-standing myths about autistic people is that they lack empathy. You will find this myth endorsed by medical professionals alarmingly frequently. In reality, studies have shown that autistic people have the same level of emotional empathy as non-autistic people but can have difficulty with cognitive empathy, which is when you predict or know how someone else will be feeling.[82]

For example, when I was young and had friends over, I was constantly chastised by my mum for not offering them things. When I was really young, I would even get myself a drink and not them. However, once I knew or understood that they wanted a drink, I would gladly have given them the last can of Coke on earth. This isn't down to a deficit so much as different wiring. It wasn't that it didn't occur to me that my friend could want a drink – of course he may. What struck me as insane was that, if you wanted a drink, you wouldn't simply ... ask for one? Do I have to ask my friend if he needs the toilet? Shall I blink his eyes for him? To me, once you came over as my friend, you could relax! Wasn't that the point? This was when I was a

82   Warrier, V., Toro, R., Chakrabarti, B. *et al.* (2018). 'Genome-wide analyses of self-reported empathy: correlations with autism, schizophrenia, and anorexia nervosa'. *Translational Psychiatry* 8, 35. https://doi.org/10.1038/s41398-017-0082-6

child and still had my natural lack of inhibitions. When I was thirsty at a friend's house, I just asked for something! Why wouldn't I? I would ask *extremely formally*, lots of pleases and thank yous, but I would still ask. It was only as I got older and began getting things wrong socially that I learned to be inhibited and the value of checking in with people through offering them things, asking them things and so on. However, the appearance of a lack of empathy was created through a different (but entirely logical) approach to manners. It is more akin to a cultural difference.

Not only is it a myth that autistic people lack empathy, it obscures the fact that often it is the non-autistic people who fail the empathy test. Let's imagine two people who work in an office. An autistic person and their non-autistic boss. The autistic employee spends huge amounts of energy masking their autism to ensure that their co-workers are comfortable around them socially. For example, they don't discuss things that are interesting to them, and cut themselves short in conversation, to guarantee they don't accidentally bore people. They may wear a suit, a shirt and tie, or put on make-up to comply with an office dress code in spite of a sensory issue that makes these things very uncomfortable for them. They force themselves to make eye contact with everyone at work. They learn how to speak the language of Small Talk fluently. They even agree to socialise after work despite being exhausted in order to seem agreeable and not jeopardise their prospects of advancement.[83] They do all this purely out of an

---

83   Obviously, this sort of thing isn't a party for anyone, but it is *more* tiring for the autistic and they are more ostracised for being themselves. If you are reading about how agonising and algorithmically predictable I find small talk and saying, 'But that's what everyone thinks!' then buddy, can I recommend you do some autism tests.

understanding of others' needs and a wish to cater to them. It seems ludicrous to say that such a person is unempathetic when they are working their bollocks off to make others comfortable. It is simply that the empathy is invisible to non-autistic eyes. When the employer forces these things upon the autistic person, maybe overrides or plays down their concerns, where is *their* empathy?

Of course, both humans are likely to be equally empathetic. It's just that these two people may have no comprehension of one another whatsoever. The difference arises when we realise that the autistic person is *forced* into comprehension and fitting in with *everyone else* and not the other way around. The non-autistic boss will never be forced contextually to learn, over a period of years of agonising failure, the ins and outs of the autistic approach to reality. He will never want to interrupt small talk to slowly lower a bin over his head until the person speaking to him leaves. The brutal truth of it is that autistic people are more likely to understand, or be forced to try to understand, non-autistic people than the other way around.

This leads us to the 'double empathy problem' theory. The term was coined by Dr Damian Milton in 2012 and he summarised it for the National Autistic Society as follows: 'Simply put, the theory of the double empathy problem suggests that when people with very different experiences of the world interact with one another, they will struggle to empathise with each other.'[84] Dr Milton's theory basically points out that empathy is a pipe that flows in both directions.

---

84 Dr Damian Milton, 2018: https://www.autism.org.uk/advice-and-guidance/professional-practice/double-empathy

The problem with old tests was that they focused on whether an autistic person shared or understood a non-autistic feeling and, when they didn't, slapped them with the 'low empathy' label. However, the test never bothered seeing if the non-autistic person could understand or share an autistic feeling and, when you do test the non-autistic person, they can't either. The lack of empathy is *mutual*. When the tests are done using two autistic people, their understanding and empathy scores are about as high as when two non-autistic people do the test with each other. In other words, autistic people have 'normal' levels of empathy for other autistic people and the same 'low empathy' for non-autistic people as non-autistic people have for *them*.[85]

It might sound obvious now but it was hugely significant: it upends decades' worth of thinking about how to approach autism. For years one of the central ideas about autism was that autistic people were deficient in that they had no theory of mind, or that they had 'mind blindness' – an inability to perceive or understand what could be going through someone else's mind. This dehumanised autistic people, made them seem immoral or untrustworthy, made it easier to be cruel to them and allowed various misapprehensions about autism to take root and spread throughout the medical profession for decades: you can't be autistic because you have friends, or are funny, or are kind, or generous, or work helping people, or enjoy music or theatre or art, because all of these

---

85 Autistic people having normal empathy and understanding for each other may also explain how often autistic people cluster together socially, even unknowingly. I was diagnosed by my friend Fern, though I ignored it for years, because she got diagnosed. Now that I am diagnosed, it turns out that four of my closest friends score high on autism quotient tests and some are now diagnosed.

things require emotion and empathy and autistic people don't have those.

The old idea was that, due to developmental delays or other problems, autistic people suffered 'an extreme form of egocentrism with the resulting lack of consideration for others,' to quote an academic. It is impossible for me to read that sentence without reading it as a blistering moral condemnation, an accusation of total moral and philosophical deficiency. This is categorically not how the academic intended it, but what else would a non-academic take from such extraordinary phrasing? If you genuinely, in your heart and soul, are so thrilled by the bus timetables of pre-war Berlin that it makes you feel as if you could fly, is it egocentrism to try and explain or share that incredible feeling with someone else? Or is it an honest mistake driven by good intentions? Naïve, certainly, but not negative, not unless the person has already made their anti-bus timetable feelings clear. Again, we must ask: Who is lacking empathy here? Who is being sincere? The irony is that the very people who view autistic people as deficient in empathy are themselves being less empathetic.

The studies that 'proved' autistic people lack theory of mind and empathy have either been refuted, shown failure of replication or show mixed results, but not before they could be cited and used in teaching materials around the world for years. The articulation of the double empathy problem by Dr Milton is part of the much-needed fightback. It makes the argument for *reciprocal* understanding and has been accepted even by many of the previous generation of academics who believed in the deficit of theory of mind. To say nothing of the fact that it has been repeatedly shown to be true in scientific studies.[86]

Don't mistake this fightback against the empathy myth for an attempt to prove that autism is not a disability, or disabling. There are plenty of other issues that arise from having autism that exist. We can't get too excited about erasing the idea of autism as a disability, because it may negatively impact the argument for further provision for autistic people with a greater level of need. I can easily imagine a desperate government minister, frantically searching for things to cut, being told that autism isn't a disability at all. Their face would light up with joy as they removed provision for autistic people from every budget imaginable and I cannot deny that, aside from making me vaguely sad, this would not affect me. I do not (currently) rely on any state provision and nor are my autistic needs particularly difficult to meet. It would be incredibly selfish of me to risk the help that others depend upon in some attempt to make myself seem 'more normal'.

Then again, if autism is about having too much of something versus too little, there could be an argument that while some autistic people with empathy are worse at guessing or 'knowing' what others feel, there might be some with an overabundance of empathy. Autistic people often anthropomorphise or assign personality traits to objects, for example. Remember when you were a kid and you felt sad if one stuffed animal was left out? That, but for potentially any object and even as an adult. Studies have shown that autistic

---

86   Milton, Damian EM, Waldock, Krysia Emily and Keates, Nathan (2023). 'Autism and the "double empathy problem".' *Conversations on Empathy: Interdisciplinary Perspectives on Empathy, Imagination and Othering* : 78–97.

people can have deep empathy and understanding for animals compared with the general population, like famous naturalist Chris Packham.

There is a test, one of the original tests used to show that autistic people were deficient in theory of mind, where participants see a close-up photo of someone's eyes and must choose a word which best describes what that person is thinking or feeling. Your test score is affected by how many answers you get right but also by how long you take, since autistic people could get the right answers but take longer analysing a photo whereas non-autistic people might immediately sense or know the answer. A study from 2022 showed that autistic and neurotypical people scored about the same on this test using the classic photos but, when the photos of the eyes were substituted for cartoon versions of the eyes, autistic people scored better than neurotypical people. It was the first study to show autistic people out-performing neurotypical in this test and could imply that at some stage empathy development in the brain specialises towards humans only in neurotypicals and stays somehow broader or non-human-specific in autistics.

My armchair theory is also that human eyes in a photo might be as triggering and overwhelming to autistics as they can be in real life, whereas cartoon eyes are not, and so the removal of an instinctive social anxiety response improved test scores by allowing the autistic people to feel more confident of their answers and less instinctively under pressure. The test is called 'Reading the Mind in the Eyes' and I recommend giving it a go online – staring at photos of eyes and answering questions on a time limit makes you feel like you're solving some sinister riddle in a thriller.

I do not think that autism makes one more empathetic, simply that empathy is often the result of repeated suffering and so it is with autistic people. If the majority of the population were autistic, we would have had decades of cruel research into why these damn non-autistics are so unempathetic: they force small talk upon others, they eat smelly food on the train, and force everyone to constantly look them in the eyes. Truly the behaviour of egomaniacs.

And remember in the previous chapter when I discussed alexithymia? There is also a risk that autism on its own has nothing to do with bad theory of mind test results and that these results are simply a result of alexithymic people, autistic or otherwise, not understanding *their own* emotions to *begin with* and so being unable to predict the emotions of others. It could explain why so many of the tests that 'prove' the deficiency in theory of mind in autistic people show mixed and inconsistent results: sometimes the random sample just had more or fewer autistic people who *also* had alexithymia, and remember the co-occurrence is around 50 per cent. There's a coin flip chance that any autistic person taking the test is being undermined by a condition that is separate from autism.

As discussed, our understanding of the mind and the brain is so crude and neurodivergence is a constantly changing field. It's a sign of enormous progress that is frustrating if all you want is answers. If we are lucky, everything that everyone is writing about neurodivergence will be out of date very soon.

CHAPTER 9

Why Do I Bear Grudges?

I had no idea that grudges could be part of autism until I was messaged by a friend, fellow comedian and autistic person, Fern Brady. Fern called my autism at the same time as she got her diagnosis, but it took me years to catch up – I should have listened! Her diagnosis of me was based on when we met in 2013 and, when she was telling me about her school in Scotland, which was named after an obscure saint. I knew the saint from my studies and said so, then told her some of the early medieval myths associated with him. Not an official test but no less effective for that.

The other day she sent me some screenshots from an article about 'anger rumination' and grudges in autism and I had some 'oh, shit' moments of self-recognition while reading it. Anger rumination is a tendency to dwell on negative, frustrating experiences or past occasions where you became angry. It's a way of processing experiences that focuses on the stressor, or incident, and dwelling on distress, mistakes, regrets and shortcomings. Basically, you *cannot* stop thinking about something bad that happened. Constantly focusing on the bad thing that happened stops you from getting over the bad thing, stops you from looking at it from a different angle or maybe somehow solving the problem that caused it. Instead of getting over a grudge or figuring out why a particular thing or person sets you off, you'll simply repeat the anger part of the experience by getting angry all over again. It's like the original incident was some writing in pen on your arm and your obsessive rumination is tattooing that writing onto your flesh forever. It's very 'villain origin story' behaviour.

This looping and obsessive dwelling is part of something called perseveration and is defined as 'an inappropriate repetition of some behaviour or thought or speech' or 'an inability to switch ideas', even to the extent that in an interview a patient may continue to give the same responses to later questions as he did to earlier ones – for example, continuing to respond to 'How are you?' during subsequent, different questions. It is not exclusively an autistic phenomenon and appears in people with ADHD, OCD, PTSD, traumatic brain injury or certain neurological diseases.[87] Basically, if something has made your brain wiring odd, you might get stuck every now and then.

You might irrationally fear a past event returning, be unable to get over anger or fear, repeat questions or answers over and over, obsessively go over conversations in your mind, repeat a physical action or repeatedly talk about something that happened a long time ago. This matters because, big surprise, *constantly* obsessing over anger, failure and regret

---

87 Cannot read this without adding in 'and much, much more!' in a television announcer's voice.

could make you depressed. *Constantly* re-analysing negative social interactions like some sort of shame VAR referee can make your anxiety a lot worse. If you ruminate on the one time that you left the gas hob on by accident and it caused a huge argument, it could develop into an obsessive-compulsive habit of checking over and over again.

Now, I like to think I've become pretty Zen as an adult, especially since the pandemic, but in the past? I could bear a grudge like a fucking *samurai*. I remember a guy called Tim in the year above me used to push into the lunch queue with his gang of friends using a combination of audacity and physical intimidation. At the time, no one was exactly pleased about it, but with my autistic rigidity regarding rules and fairness? The idea that not only was something unfair happening but that the villain was making me wait *even longer* in the boring queue, I was incandescent with powerless rage. I am amazed my head didn't light up like a bulb. The last time one of these incidents occurred I was fifteen years old and I didn't stop getting a flash of anger when I remembered it until maybe ten years later.

When I say a flash of anger, I need to make it clear that I mean a flash of anger *for real*. As in, a flash of anger as if it was happening again. I don't mean 'Oh yes, I remember not liking that.' What I mean is that by remembering it I re-experience it to an extent that neurotypical people would not.

Autistic people seem to often have a more intense memory than non-autistic people.[88] There are a lot of studies about various areas of the brain lighting up during memory tests

88 Zamoscik, V., Mier, D., Schmidt, S.N. and Kirsch, P. 'Early Memories of Individuals on the Autism Spectrum Assessed Using Online Self-Reports'. *Front Psychiatry*. May 2;7:79. DOI: 10.3389/fpsyt.2016.00079. PMID: 27199786; PMCID: PMC4852178.

but the science is so new it feels a bit 'tea leaves', but let's just say that if you are autistic and can memorise thousands of tiny social rules instead of knowing them instinctively, you probably develop a hell of a memory. For example, we left South Africa when I was six years old and I remembered our full address, phone number and the layout of my school and our old house until I was in my late teens.

How fabulous, you might think, to have a good memory. Except it is inconsistent and only works for, say, faces and not names. More importantly, you are *supposed* to forget. I think that's one of the ways that social media has driven us loopy – you aren't *supposed* to know what those kids from your primary school are up to! That's too many people to remember! You're not supposed to be able to vividly remember what it was like to be angry with someone ten years ago, what it was like to be in love with someone ten years ago, what it was like to be afraid of someone ten years ago. The mind is supposed to move on, to paint new scenes over those old murals, at least to some extent. If we all remembered everything all of the time forever, we'd go insane.

The trouble is that, during the ten years of anger rumination on this lunch queue guy, my memory meant that the experience stayed vivid. Not completely vivid, but I could make myself angry all over again by remembering it. Let's say 70 per cent as angry compared to how angry I was at the time. A loud echo.

This is something of a social impediment. If you cannot *ever* forget people's negative actions towards you, it completely destroys your ability to forgive, to move on or even befriend them. It forces you to choose between coming across as a bitter, angry person or spending energy masking your true feelings by pretending you aren't affected at all, which will breed resentment and probably make you even more annoyed. It makes you more anxious and stressed about future negative events happening because you know that they will be a ten-year problem as opposed to a 'have a pint and a laugh and get over it' problem. You also may ascribe the same behaviour to others and fear your own behaviour too. I once apologised to someone for being short with them during a stressful show rehearsal at university a full five years after it happened. They had no idea what I was talking about[89] and I had been stressed, sad and regretful about it every single time I had seen or thought about them for five years. Needlessly stressful and a huge waste of energy.

If you're autistic, it also makes it impossible to figure out what might or might not stick in the mind of a neurotypical person. I am always surprised by the nice things people remember about me, because I don't remember them, and I am often surprised by the things that upset people, because they are rarely what I'd be upset by. This means that not only do you worry about your own grudges and others, you are aware on an even higher level that your grudges and regrets might not even *make sense to anyone else.* That thing you obsessively regret? The person doesn't even remember. That other thing that you did without thinking and did not feel was significant? The person has a tattoo of it and is going to kill you someday. It feels impossible to predict which is which and adds a lovely extra layer of The Unknown to the whole situation. How can

---

89 Or did they?! Oh God! Non-autistic people lie out of politeness all the time, so was that a lie? I'll never know, so I must cross it off the list for my own sanity.

you fit in with non-autistic society when you don't even realise what other people dislike and remember, and you have no faith that any of your own dislikes are even legitimate?

If you decide to hold fast and indulge your memory, eventually your list of grudges, regrets, fears and failures becomes so long that you feel like your only option is to live in a very tall, spindly tower in the forest. The other option is to decide 'Fuck it, I'll do my best but never worry, and I won't bother worrying about others' bad behaviour either.' Then blunder your way through life utterly unrepentant and shutting out your own thoughts completely. Like a reality star who claims they 'tell it like it is'. This is another example of 'Caesar or nothing' behaviour. I have certainly tried the blundering option, attempting to save energy and reduce stress, fear, anxiety and anger by simply deciding to move on abruptly from all sorts of personal and professional relationships like some antisocial Jason Bourne skipping town. There's no easy solution here, unfortunately, and the best option is the most arduous one, a constant struggle to self-improve and be honest with others and yourself. Bleurgh! Awful! It's basically signing up to a lifetime of failure. I'd rather live in the tower in the forest but then how would I do gigs?

It could also be the case that, if you are autistic, you were just more affected by the incident to begin with. A lot of events that are traumatic to autistic people are not to non-autistic people, and vice versa. You aren't traumatised or bearing a grudge because you are autistic, but because the profound hurt or trauma was real to you, the same way it feels real to a non-autistic person in another situation. It's just that the specific sensitivity is as a result of autism. If your autism compels you to have everything organised and someone at school continuously rearranges your things, empties your rucksack onto the floor, hides your pens or whatever, it will be correspondingly more traumatic than if you were non-autistic. This leaves autistic people open to accusations of oversensitivity and, while everyone is capable of being oversensitive, there's a strong chance the autistic person cannot help it.

There is also the chance that grudge-bearing makes more sense if, having grown up autistic, you have had your own needs, wants and fears constantly ignored, belittled or undermined. That's certainly enough to make anyone bitter and there is an argument (popular online) for excluding people from your life who cannot bring themselves to see the world from your autistic, minority perspective. You *can't* change and they *won't* change, so why not save the energy of keeping them in your life and cut them out of it? It's not sociable but it certainly saves energy.

You will also have an understandably large reservoir of resentment available to you simply by virtue of being autistic in a non-autistic society. I went through a phase of anger and resentment after my diagnosis where it finally hit me: none of these non-autistic people were having to do what I do. My whole life I had vaguely assumed that a large percentage of people, if not a majority, were like me and here was proof that I was completely wrong. It was like growing up with rocks in my shoes every day and presuming that everyone else had these rocks, too. I was really resentful that no one else had these painful shoes to wear for the rest of their lives, just me and the rest of the neurodivergent gang. I was dealing with the realisations that I will never be able to be truly 'normal'.

WHY CAN'T I JUST ENJOY THINGS?

I can force myself to appear normal, but my actual *mind* and the way I *think* and *perceive* will never, ever match up to the way most people's do. Many people will see me as inherently deficient, with all the moral condemnation that sneaks in along with that judgement. It's a hell of a hard thing to accept with grace and it's fair enough to take it badly.

Unfortunately, you've got to work through that 'grieving process' before you can build your new sense of self, so as much as you are 'justified' to feel bitter and it is 'fair' to feel that way and 'unfair' to have to get over it, there is simply no other good option. You can either leave the bitter swamp or drown in it.[90]

It might be tolerable to have a computer-level memory for negative events if you also had a computer-level memory for positive events, but sadly it seems to be a party for bad vibes only. It helps, when you're having a good time, to take a moment to try to 'seal' the memory in your mind. It feels a little contrived but the more you do it, the more it becomes automatic and the more you'll start to use that memory of yours for good instead of evil.

As much as I bear grudges more than most people due to autism or factors arising from autism, I have to say, I am helpless in the face of a sincere and moving apology. Maybe it's something about the rules being followed, maybe it's the humanity of it, maybe it's proof that the person now understands and has changed their ways, I don't know. I remember the first time I experienced one of those apologies.

---

90   If you want to see how pointless and miserable it is to live in bitterness as an autistic person, take a look at some online forums. You'll find a lot of autistic people justifying their infinite grudge matches and none of them are happy. Forums like Reddit are a source of absolute gold when it comes to autism but they are also home to some of the most desperate, depressed people out there, so be careful whose posts you take to heart.

WHY DO I BEAR GRUDGES?

There was an older guy at school who was very arrogant, aloof and exclusionary to the dorks. He was very charismatic and funny, very popular, which made him likeable, but he would never show those sides directly to people who were socially less worthwhile. It was a confusing combination, odder than just being directly unpleasant, and years and years later, when I was an older teen, I bumped into this guy at a house party. The house party was hosted by someone who he had not necessarily respected back in the day and I felt it was maybe insincere for him to attend, plus I'd probably had about six cans, so I got his attention when I passed him in the corridor outside the bathroom and said, 'You know what, you were a real *cunt* to people back in the day.' I think part of me really wanted a confrontation, to make sure that this guy knew that people remembered, or at least that I did, and that it couldn't just melt away. Plus, you know, six cans and a with-hindsight autistic obsession with justice and plain-speaking.

He looked a little taken aback and said, 'Yeah, you know what? I really was' and proceeded to explain how embarrassed he was when he remembered what he had been like. It absolutely blew my mind. The second those initial words hit my ears I felt every single lingering negative thought, every grudge and every drop of resentment that had built up over the years like mould evaporate in an instant. Gone. I felt like a huge weight had been lifted off me and then I think I apologised for my tone and we had a great conversation. Ever since then I've been in awe of people who are that self-aware and able to express themselves under pressure like that and I have aspired (and failed) to be like that.

It also gave me something very valuable: from then on I

could simply presume that those who had been arseholes knew it and remembered it. That presumption saved me having to bother with a grudge, to bother to remember it myself and to bother confronting them. I felt safer from then on to think 'well, either they know they were an arsehole or they *still* don't and if they don't, they're probably stuck like that for life'.

One of the advantages of knowing you are autistic is having a better handle on how your mind works so it is easier to influence yourself, to change. I know that my mind responds very well to logic and so I can use my logical assumptions about people's growth over time, their regrets and the universal embarrassment we almost all feel about our past to presume progress and change on their part in the same way that I would like them to presume that about me. I also logically know that there is almost always no point in holding onto the emotion of a grudge, especially if you aren't going to do anything about it.

Some of you reading this will wonder: but what about the *bastards*, Pierre? The genuinely evil-seeming fuckers who not only do not grow, regret or learn but seem to relish their terribleness? The ones where it is impossible and maybe even dangerous for us to presume they've changed their ways? That's easy. Forgive but do not forget. Besides, if they really are that evil, you can't save them or change them by force anyway. There's nothing you can do and they're stuck like that; that is their most direct punishment. Hack your minds, fellow autistics, read around forgiveness and philosophy, get religious if you need to, or Zen, whatever works. It's not worth turning your mind into a prison cell.

CHAPTER 10

Meltdowns and Shutdowns

An autistic person, when they are overwhelmed by sensory issues as described elsewhere in this book, can completely overload with stress. This can also happen when they have to process too much information or emotional news at once. The stimuli that trigger it could also be big life changes, unexpected changes in plans or routine, too much social interaction or feeling overwhelmed by demands (however that looks to each person). The triggers can be internal too: shame or guilt, feeling like a failure or feeling like a victim of an injustice (that love of fairness again!). Basically, when life gives you so many lemons that they jam the blender. Autistic people can react with a meltdown or a shutdown, an explosion or an implosion.

A meltdown is what you might expect: screaming, shouting, ranting; there can also be physical lashing out, maybe at people, objects or furniture, even self-harm. These can be very distressing for the autistic person and anyone around them. It's important to note that meltdowns are *not* the same as losing your temper, for an adult, or a tantrum for a kid. Losing your temper doesn't necessarily mean losing control, as an adult, and tantrums from kids can be cynical or bribed away. A meltdown is an extreme state of anxiety that has no other way to be expressed by an autistic person whose system has been overwhelmed. They are flooded with adrenaline, the meltdowns can often last for as long as twenty minutes even after the removal of the trigger, they can be physically exhausting and autistic people may not fully remember what happened. A meltdown will mean that the autistic person is out of control in a way that losing one's temper doesn't generally involve. I would say that a meltdown is more like becoming the Hulk or a werewolf than a brief display of garden-variety 'anger'.

These days, I am an implosion man. Just call me Xi Jinping 'cause I just love to shut down, baby! When I was younger, I remember things that with hindsight seem like meltdowns, but if they were physical it was definitely more a 'punching the hell out of a pillow' scenario. I think this is partially luck of the draw that I don't feel them as externally as some autistic people, partially to do with heavy socialisation. You see, I was always bigger and stronger than other kids, and it always got me into trouble. My parents drilled it into me over and over again, even with play fighting: never do anything physical because you'll be blamed, it'll look worse simply because it's you, and you don't know your own strength and could hurt someone more than you realise. I also grew up with two sisters, one older, one younger, so after the age of about nine or ten

I was too strong to play fight with them and had to resort to annoying them with (echo) The Power of the Mind, mind, mind ... I was completely and utterly convinced about not only the uselessness of physically lashing out but also the certainty that it would make everything universally worse for me.

The last time I definitely remember having a meltdown of some kind and reacting physically was after the incident described in Chapter 9 where that guy pushed into the lunch queue for the millionth time, physically intimidating anyone who stood against him. I think I tried to say something, confront him, but I failed. I was so furious at the injustice that I felt my body go cold and shaky. I left the lunch queue, went to an empty school bathroom, punched a cubicle door and sat on the toilet lid with my whole body tensed, jaw clenched, teeth cracking away. I suddenly had a kind of third-party awareness that I was definitely *too angry*. I felt like it was a bad idea to be this angry. I had this sense that I had to calm down, if only because if I didn't my fucking head would fall off. I don't think I've ever been that angry since, not to that level. Also, I am an enormous adult man now, and if I went around smashing things I would be, at best, violently restrained by some authority figure. So, for one or all of these reasons, any physical manifestation of a meltdown or shutdown had to be ruthlessly suppressed.

After that, it's only really shutdowns I remember. The tortoise head goes into the shell. A shutdown is still a response to extreme overload or stress – the stimuli that cause a meltdown are the same that cause a shutdown. The response is muted and the distress stays internal. When I shutdown, I feel more like when you see a big snake in a documentary digesting an entire antelope, just so full of this big lumpy problem you're amazed it's not bursting, and having to spend days and days perfectly still, trying to break it down, digest it, absorb it. I will generally go silent, withdraw from whatever is going on, either into my own head or, in my dream scenario, physically withdraw and lie down in a dark room on my own. That would be the dream but, unfortunately, the person you are arguing with does tend to follow you into the dark room and stop you from lying down in silence. Ho-hum. Then again, physically freezing or being 'stuck' is also part of a shutdown.

Remember in the old days when you asked too much of your home PC and its hard drive went from going *vrrrrr* to going *VEEEEE!* and everything froze? And the side of the computer got worryingly hot? That's what's happening to my brain. It has too much to process and, while it tries to, it will have to shut down a lot of the external stuff. It takes a while to emerge from shutdowns and, when I do, I generally feel so exhausted that I fall straight asleep or want to. I don't just mean 'Oh, I'm tired', I mean full-on silly cartoon shit. Eyelids drooping, head-nodding, like the ridiculous sleepiness of an irresponsible guard outside the hero's jail cell. Pure exhaustion all from the extreme physiological reaction to stress.

If an autistic person has a meltdown, you should give them time and space to recover and, if you can identify it, remove or reduce the trigger for the meltdown. This presumes of course that, if you are an autistic person, the people around you have any understanding of what is going on and, if they do understand, they are compassionate. Add to that the anxiety of wondering if they will hold it against you, have lost respect for you, and you're well on your way to building up enough stress for your next one. It also doesn't help if it's caused by having an argument – it doesn't make much emotional sense for the person arguing with you to suddenly become your nurse.

I've also been in a few situations where my silent shutdown and withdrawal was mistaken for some sort of magnificent silent fury, which certainly didn't help. I'm lucky, however, since my shutdowns are triggered almost exclusively by fraught emotional conversations. It is far, far harder to deal with a meltdown, especially a physical one that involves lashing out, when it is triggered by something less private like an overcrowded train or being disciplined unfairly by an employer.

If this happens to you then the best course of action, recommended online and by my meltdown-having autistic friends, is to learn the signs of an approaching meltdown or the 'rumble stage'. This will give you an early warning as well as, possibly, a chance of preventing the meltdown entirely. For the best results you should figure out, if you don't already know, what calms you down so you can do it at this stage. Lying down in a dark room under a weighted blanket, maybe. It's also useful to keep a diary to maintain a constant and careful analysis of why you melt down – there are apps available for this kind of thing as well as good old-fashioned pen and paper. Keeping a diary could reveal patterns that you were not aware of, for example that you have a meltdown at work on Mondays if you drink alcohol on Saturdays but not on Fridays because Sunday is an extra day for recovery, or you only meltdown in a specific train station because of how busy it gets compared to others.

Once you've done the detective work, you can minimise

the triggers. I have managed to save myself a lot of stress in general by getting some noise-cancelling headphones and allowing myself to be a little later for an appointment if the tube train that arrives first is too busy for me to tolerate. If you are the partner or family member of someone who has meltdowns, it might be very difficult not to take the lashing out, verbal or physical, personally, but it might also help to keep in mind that they are an involuntary response from someone who would definitely rather *not* have them.

Make sure you do research externally – autism resources are available online, for free, at a generally very high quality – as well as figuring out what makes you tick internally, and you too could hack your mind for maximum contentment. Or, to put it less like an Instagram ad for dodgy brain pills, you too could be happier.

CHAPTER 11

Why Can't I Get Anything Done?

I am writing this chapter at the very start of writing this book. I am finding it incredibly difficult to start working on it and so it seemed appropriate to force myself to start with the exact cause of my difficulties: executive dysfunction. It also struck me that maybe I'd do a better job of describing it when I was up to my bloody eyeballs in it, desperate to work but paralysed by stress.

I had never heard of the term 'executive dysfunction' until sometime during lockdown 2020, long before my diagnosis. Live comedy performances were illegal and my industry was devastated, so, on the advice of wise and kind Iain Stirling, I took up Twitch streaming. Basically, you play videogames and try to be funny and people watch you. The money comes from advertising, donations and pay-to-play elements. One of my regulars had mentioned in the chat that she was having a particularly bad period of executive dysfunction lately, so I asked what it was and the chatroom did its best to explain it to me. I looked it up, as I do with all things, and didn't immediately recognise it in me, which seems insane in hindsight.

Executive dysfunction appears regularly in a wide range of conditions. It appears not only in cases of neurodivergence like autism or ADHD, but also in Parkinson's, schizophrenia and various other neurological, mental health and behavioural disorders. Executive dysfunction is most easily defined as the impairment of your executive functions.

A quick internet search yields the following definition of executive functions from *Medical News Today*:

Analysing and processing information

Managing emotions and behaviour

Remembering details

Multitasking

Solving problems

Managing time

Planning and organisation

Concentrating and managing mental focus.

I think what must have happened, and which happened throughout any early attempts by me to understand what was different about my brain, is that I could easily think of examples where my executive function worked just fine and I would use that to rule myself out as a potentially autistic person.

Analysing and processing information? That's all I do! Could someone with a weird brain become *this* obsessed with Bronze Age excavations in modern-day Turkey over an afternoon? I think not, sir!

WHY CAN'T I GET ANYTHING DONE?

Managing emotions and behaviour? Hmm, well, maybe when I was small, but that's little kids for you, isn't it? As an adult I'd say that all I do is spend my entire day managing my emotions and my behaviour. I think I'm ninja-level skilled at that by now. After all, I sat next to that guy eating crisps with his mouth open for an entire train journey, boiling with rage, and I didn't make a peep! And earlier, when that barista asked me if I was having a good day, I just said yes! I completely swallowed my urge/instinct to answer honestly and say, 'I have no idea what you, specifically, mean by the word "good", I don't know you nearly well enough to answer.' Cool as a cucumber.

Remembering details? OK, it took me years to memorise the birthdays of people close to me and often I still fail. That sort of detail is hard, but it's been over a decade and I can still remember the full plot, names and quotes from every single book I studied in sixth form. I can remember multiple hours of stand-up, down to specific syllabic intonations. People famously enjoy it when I remember, word for word, their opinions from university that they now find extremely embarrassing.

Multitasking and solving problems? Even as I write this I am keeping up to date on a square-kilometre-level with the war in Ukraine, drinking a coffee, listening to music, checking emails and desperately trying to write a book. Case closed!

Managing time? Look, if I didn't spend three hours reading about the aforementioned Bronze Age archaeology, would I have had the energy to rush through my tasks at the last minute? I like to assume the answer is no? OK, fair point.

Planning and organising? Maybe you've got me there. I remember in French classes in school I adopted a, forgive me, laissez-faire approach to things. I would show up with genuinely no idea if I had the relevant books, worksheets, or even pens in my bag and when asked to produce them, treated my bag as a big Christmas cracker that may well contain the desired homework, but equally could contain a tiny set of screwdrivers. But I got over that, didn't I? After all, as a stand-up, I run a small business! Ah, but I am often late to book trains, I fill out my tax returns at death's door, my invoicing is ... well, I am sure someone out there still owes me money. OK, guilty.

Concentrating and managing mental focus – this is another mixed one. I can clearly concentrate. The bored listeners to my rant about Bronze Age archaeology in modern-day Turkey can attest to the fruits of my concentration. I do find it hard to swing the laser beam of concentration at the right target at the right time. I have been fortunate in my life in that I have been able, generally, to trick my obsessive brain into getting obsessed with the right things at the right times. It's like tricking your kids into thinking mopping floors and hoovering is fun by letting them do it dressed as Batman. I would dress as Batman if I thought it would make me more productive, but it would probably distract everyone else trying to work in the café.

Like so much medical self-research, my ability to discern whether or not I had executive dysfunction was hamstrung by my lack of external guidance on what examples actually meant, or the different ways it might manifest. One of the main reasons I initially refused to believe that I had any significant executive dysfunction was down to my academic record. However, looking back now, there were many obvious (non-academic) signs of my executive dysfunction, a reminder that exam results are a photograph of a child's progress and not a film.

Between the ages of two and six my educators were briefly concerned that I was undiagnosed deaf. I would be playing or doing something and would seem not to hear any instructions and be completely unaware of even loud sounds. It's hard to tell if this was executive dysfunction, in terms of being unable to concentrate on instruction, or a sign of early hyperfocus. My friend, the actor Jason Forbes, once thought I was utterly furious with him when we were at university because I was sitting on a bench reading a book and he approached me and asked me what I was reading. I said nothing and kept reading. He asked a couple more questions to absolute silence before walking off, stung. I have no recollection of this whatsoever and only remember reading my book, in which I was completely engrossed. I did not hear, see or perceive him in any way, shape or form. It was an uncomfortable conversation later on when I walked over to him and some friends and Jason explained how he'd had to walk away awkwardly after I ignored everything he said and how worried he'd been that I suddenly hated him. I did my best to explain that, yes, that can happen sometimes with me, using my alleged childhood deafness as an example, but I could see I was not fully convincing him that I wasn't secretly furious with him. Misunderstandings upon misunderstandings! All we can do is beg to be understood and hope that others believe us.

My father reminded me recently that on the train to my Cambridge interview I was studying my notes intently. The train stopped and was delayed with the automatic brake coming on. It then had to reverse slowly back to the nearest station. We got off and had to wait for a replacement train. Apparently I got off the train, zombie-like with notes in hand, leaving my bag and laptop for my dad to carry. When we arrived, my dad commented that the journey was the longest 'fast train' he'd ever experienced. 'Why?' I asked. I had no idea (and no memory) that we had stopped, got off, or got on another train.

This is the potential crossover between executive dysfunction and hyperfocus – it would be executive dysfunction if, in that scenario, my job was to listen to Jason. It becomes hyperfocus if, in that scenario, we decide that reading the book was vital in some way and Jason was a distraction. Fundamentally, a lot of positives and negatives are entirely up to us to decide. They are not fixed truths but a matter of perception. We need to be able to see through these moral judgements to a fundamental truth: I was unable to see or hear a human, standing less than a metre from me, due to something to do with my brain. I didn't *decide* to ignore him, it was not willpower or discipline, it simply happened to be the case that, to me, he did not exist and I didn't perceive him in much the same way I do not perceive ultraviolet light. Jason, if you are reading this, I apologise for comparing your shining social presence to light that's invisible to the human eye and I completely understand your baffled scepticism.

In fact, this crossover is the source of a lot of the neurotypical scepticism directed towards neurodivergent people. I would, in a moment of honesty or catharsis, say to a neurotypical friend that I was a useless creature who couldn't get things done and that I needed to sort my shit out. The first problem, as always, would be that the neurotypical would interpret this statement as a disguised cry for reassurance, disguised because it is unacceptable to grab someone by the shoulders and say, 'Tell me I am good. Tell me I am good at things.' So, instead, neurotypical people sometimes performatively criticise themselves to trigger a sympathetic intervention. I'm not doing that – the statement is a perfectly sincere description of my situation. Secondly, they would say that I am being silly and that of course I get things done – after all, how else had I done my many hour-long stand-up shows, written a novel in lockdown, recorded and edited all those podcasts etc?

They don't understand that those things are in the hyperfocus/obsession category generally and that I am, to an extent, compelled to do them. When I said I was useless I was referring, say, to the fact that I have owned a fancy pair of wireless headphones for over a year and have been insisting on using them with a wire even though the wire keeps catching on things and getting in the way and needs an adaptor for my phone anyway, an adaptor I keep losing. A daily, infuriating problem that would be solved instantly if I just charged my headphones and connected them with Bluetooth. If I could just summon the energy to check the left-hand-side jacket pocket I was certain I had left the charger in ...

Or how about when my flatmate and I held a US Presidents-themed New Year's Eve party and decorated the flat with bunting, a big US flag and a crappy cardboard stand of the Statue of Liberty? The cutout became known as Lizzie and she, as well as the bunting, remained proud symbols of freedom in our flat for four more years. We both agreed we needed to do something about the bunting, and about Lizzy (particularly as she had developed a hinge-crease in her face which made her look furious, as though neither I nor my flatmate had embodied the idea of liberty nearly enough in daily life), but despite our agreement, we did nothing. It just *felt* like too big a job, even though it would take seconds. The same goes for my three-year delay in hanging up some pictures in the flat – I only got that done because I was procrastinating from writing the very book you are reading and even then it only took an hour. Three-year delay! My God! Sort yourself out!

The hardest thing is to explain to people how big these tasks seem. Sometimes it feels as though my brain has got its telescope reversed and big things seem doable and small things don't. Write a novel by yourself? Sure, fine, easy. Pick up that coat that's been on the floor for two weeks? Jeeze, I don't know, I've got a lot on, I'm so tired I have begun to accept that there will never be an easy way to explain, viscerally, how this feels. I am afraid the best I can do is say to you, 'Small things feel like big things' and hope you accept that. If not, you will be forced to confront the paradox between thinking of me as lazy and untidy on one hand and on the other accepting that I get a lot of things done and that my entire flat has a system of organisation for all kitchen items and books.

Maybe the reason is that part of being autistic is having to think things out longhand when other people use short-hand or don't think at all – I can't turn off my brain. It's always thinking, so if it's thinking during a boring task, it's actively thinking about how bored it is, how boring the task is, and how long it's taking. Maybe that's one reason for aversion to simple but boring tasks and the love of huge but complex tasks – one doesn't stimulate and one does.

WHY CAN'T I GET ANYTHING DONE?

It's tough to compete with the social idea, shoved into us at school, that any reason one might give for not getting something done is essentially laziness. That unless your task was blocked by the performance of another task, you are merely being lazy and must be punished or shamed. I am keenly aware that, to sceptics, I seem like someone saying, 'I am sorry I did not pick up my socks, you see, I am too mental to pick up socks', but if they aren't willing to try to empathise there is nothing we can do for them.

I was always very aware that I was, in terms of efficiency and tasks, broadly useless. A teacher had to point out to me, aged eight, that perhaps I would copy the words down from the board faster and more neatly if I held the entire word in my head and wrote it all at once, as opposed to letter by letter like some medieval scribe. This awareness was a large part of why I was so keen on joining the military when I was young. I had grown up around men who had spent time in the military and they all spoke about how, though it was very tough, it did set them up in terms of habits. These men had superpowers I could only dream of as a teenager: waking up automatically at a good time, swiftly ironing their clothes, a dedication to physical fitness – the ability to roll up their sleeves completely evenly on both sides! Imagine! And thanks to the repetition of training they did all this without it registering as conscious effort – it didn't *feel* like trying.

I reasoned that if I joined the military, if only for the minimum term, I would embed these fine habits in my stupid brain and become A Serious Adult. Not only that but think of all that delicious structure! Deciding what to wear, deciding what to eat (and making it), deciding how my room should look, what I should be doing on any particular day – all of these agonisingly boring decisions would be taken care of! In some ways I cannot think of a more autistic-friendly job. The army give you clear, direct instructions about what to do and their expectations in almost every regard, and if you want to get promoted or get qualified to use a particular weapons system, drive a particular vehicle, organise a particular department, they will give you a list of what you need to do to get that particular badge. And the badges! Who is above me? The people with the bigger badges and hats. Who is under my authority? The people with the smaller badges and hats. If you get confused, here is a chart of the badges and hats. Here is the official way to Be Polite, the official way to move your arms and legs, the official way to dress. It might sound mad, but it sounded to me like paradise.

Also, all the rules were either utterly crucial in a very obvious way (don't do this to your rifle, it will explode) or they were mad and arbitrary, but crucially *admitted that they were mad and arbitrary.* It gave me an incredible sense of relief and honesty when an authority figure just admitted that the rule was there because it was there and it didn't matter why, even if it was silly. Very few other adults in civilian life, like my teachers, had the guts to admit, or to perceive, that so many of their rules were completely arbitrary.

I am not exaggerating when I say that being a cadet during my teenage years was a tremendous help to me. The sense of self-respect and practical confidence I gained was invaluable. When you are fifteen or sixteen and a veteran of tours in Afghanistan and Iraq trusts you with a rifle, or deputises you to take a gang of other kids up into the hills and set up camp, it feels like a real compliment during a time in your life when you are seen as unreliable hormonal scum and treated as such. I wasn't exaggerating earlier when I mentioned the sleeve thing, by the way. I learned, from wearing my uniform, the best way to roll up my sleeves neatly, re-lace and tie boots properly, polish shoes, stitch on badges and buttons, iron clothes and, perhaps less usefully for civilian life, shape a beret.

Looking back, I think the reason the military method was so useful for learning these things is that the army has to train people up by starting with the presumption that they know nothing about anything. There was never any presumption of knowledge, never any judgement for not knowing something or being crap (other than that we should aim to be better); there was only a very clear set of instructions, repeated a few times, on how to do something. As well as clearly communicated consequences for failing to do it, imposed from above. In adult life, it turns out that if you dress like a shambling scarecrow, all that happens is that people think less of you, and who cares about that?

That cadets taught me first aid, map and compass skills, camping skills, weapons safety, marksmanship, leadership, self-confidence – I did a sort of rudimentary teaching qualification. The first laughs I ever got from public speaking were during my exam for qualifying to teach weapons safety. I got a great laugh from Sergeant A, one of the cadet training team, for an off-the-cuff joke and I have never forgotten it. I also learned, from Captain P, the head of our training team of actual military people who visited us twice a year, how to organise myself. I was constantly losing keys, wallets, phones, documents, pens, you name it. I was often in trouble and it was hell. Once, we were on exercise with the training team on a big trip to Yorkshire, part of which was a patrol at night. Captain P explained to us that we would be expected to be able to find any piece of kit we needed at any time even in the pitch-black. I nodded thoughtfully and tried to look competent, while privately thinking, 'Well, that's never going to fucking happen – I can't find French homework *in the day*', but then Captain P explained that he only ever kept specific things in specific pockets, according to a system. He never needed to 'look' for anything, he simply reached for it. It was a revelation. The only reason I have ever been able to adequately locate my phone, wallet, keys etc. at any point in my entire life, whether in a rush, blind drunk or in the pitch-black is thanks to Captain P's system.

My instinct is that most people just, well, use their brains to remember things, so I presume that the last few paragraphs make me seem like some kind of forgetful Colonel Kurtz figure. Maybe they seem like the ramblings of a militarised toddler, I don't know. All I can tell you is that I needed an authority figure to explain a system to me, very patiently, that prevented me from being a useless fucker. That is precisely what Captain P did.

In the end I didn't join up, so I will never know if a few years in the army would have solved, through sheer training, my executive dysfunction, or if it would have ended in disaster as I produced some long-lost French homework to my commanding officer instead of a map of enemy positions.

Looking back at all the non-academic executive dysfunction is one thing, but even when it comes to academia I realise that I am very fortunate that I had my obsessive brain and memory working overtime to compensate for the bad planning and lack of discipline that, in hindsight, are such clear signs of executive dysfunction.

For example, I remember that in the run-up to one of my GCSEs, I decided arbitrarily that I could not begin to revise until I had reached a particular rank on a popular first-person shooter video game on my PC. There was no reason for this and, honestly, at that point I genuinely didn't even enjoy the game. There was something deeply compulsive about it that I still don't quite understand. I say that I decided it but it felt almost forced upon me, and it might be hard to understand as you read this, but it also felt true: it really did feel as though I couldn't start revising until the appropriate rank had been reached via the pwning of noobs.[91] The thought of simply stopping playing the game and picking up the textbook felt like skipping a vital step, as impossible as deciding to take a bite from a sandwich that you haven't made yet. Not only impossible but *illogical*. We all procrastinate, of course, and it may take the form of tidying your room or doing laundry or something productive like that, but I think if it comes with this sinister, reality-bending or compulsive aspect, you have to take it more seriously.

A friend who may or may not be on the spectrum says that, every year of his academic life, before he could possibly begin revising for finals he would have to read through *The Adventures of Tom Sawyer* in its entirety, three times. I have never related so hard to something so unrelatable before – as I heard it, I felt that I completely understood why he

---

91 The besting of less-skilled players of the videogame, a deliberate misspelling of 'owning of newbies'.

needed to do that, despite there being no causal link between the two actions of reading *The Adventures of Tom Sawyer* and revising.[92] In my opinion, it could be that these compulsions are not completely damaging and do have a purpose, however minor. It strikes me that both my videogame playing and my relative's reading and re-reading of the same book are forms of procrastination that are fundamentally boring, repetitive and involve prolonged periods of heavy concentration, as well as requiring (ironically) some self-discipline and time management. They also involve reassuring familiarity, they are the opposite of a pursuit of novelty. Could it be that these are almost hypnotic techniques designed to induce in our minds the feeling and sense of deep, boring concentration required to revise thoroughly for an exam? Are they the brain equivalent of stretching our muscles before working out? Getting in the zone? It is obviously preferable to simply have self-discipline and do things when you need to, but I tend to get self-discipline from routine and something like revising for an exam is by definition a temporary state of, what, a month? By the time I get into that routine, I've done the exam!

I remember that the teacher of that French class where I never had the right papers, texts and so on would say to me, with a knowing, doom-laden smile, 'You know, when you get to university, you won't be able to carry on like this.' 'I'll show her!' I thought. 'I'll be just as pointlessly disorganised at university and *still* get away with it! Haha! And it will almost snap my brain in half! Victory!'

I was more self-disciplined at university, but I had to be to

---

92 In fairness, this would be a fabulous way to revise for an exam on the book, *The Adventures of Tom Sawyer*. You'd be a fool to deny that.

survive the intensive workload. I studied Anglo-Saxon, Norse and Celtic Studies at the University of Cambridge and arrived as one of the few students with no fluency or familiarity with any Celtic or Germanic languages and no Latin either, so I was starting from scratch. Initially I found the hands-off nature of university quite freeing, but by the second year I had unravelled a little without structure and had become addicted to the thrill of living as I wished, without compromise, and getting away with it.

At one point, I was writing three 2,000-word essays a week on three different subjects with six to ten books cited per essay and still managing to sleep in, miss lectures and do comedy. I am obviously, naughtily proud of that simply because I got away with it, but it was a fucking awful way to live. The stress and the caffeine ground me down into a weird, furtive little freak who, due to late-night working habits, became increasingly isolated from the other people on my course and in my halls. Looking back, it was a perfect storm of executive dysfunction and autistic burnout, but at the time I figured it was pretty normal to drink six or seven black coffees at night, and spend the day sprinting from library to library, pouring sweat and jabbering to myself.

The closest I came to snapping was on a day where I had left twenty-four hours to write an essay on the appearance and disappearance of pagan symbolism from Scandinavian Iron Age graves. I had run all over town looking in libraries for the books on the weekly reading list for this essay. These were rare books and on niche topics that required a level of expertise that one cannot find on Wikipedia: I *needed* the physical books and I needed to take them *out*, so I could write in my smelly room all night. However, everyone else on my course was an actual proper person and had taken the lion's share of the reading list out of the library already. I was fucked.

I checked the list and searched in the university system for the final few books on the list and saw that they were available. Oh, sweet relief! They were hiding away in the library of the archaeology department on the other side of town. I half-ran, drenched in sweat, across town to the archaeology department, exhausted not only by the heat and the stress but by the fact that I had spent the night before – yes, you guessed it – staying up late and desperately writing a different essay. I arrived at the archaeology library looking like I was fleeing the CIA and had to sign up before I could go in. I remember droplets of sweat thwacking onto the little form as I filled it in, out of breath, standing up and bending over the librarian's desk, biro quivering in my hand. She was horrified – there are few emergencies in archaeology. Soon, I was in! I stomped through the empty library, found the books and sat with them in a triumphant pile, a sweaty, wrecked mess. I opened them and discovered that they were in Danish.

No wonder no one else had bothered checking them out. I laid my wet head carefully on the desk and took a few minutes to absorb the situation. Ultimately, thanks to online translators (though back then very unreliable), some logical deduction and careful use of the appendix of each book, I still got what I needed. I wish I could say I followed my lecturer's advice and learned academic Danish purely to further my studies, but I did not. Though I have gigged in Copenhagen and unnerved the Danes with my eerie knowledge of their early medieval history, it would have been even more fun to use some incredibly specific vocabulary to unsettle them. I could have marched confidently into some fashionable Copenhagen café, leant across the elaborate pastries and asked the barista if they knew where I could buy some prestigious, ritual grave goods.

Unfortunately, I did not learn from that situation. I should have thought, 'Gosh, what an astonishingly stressful way to live. All of these problems are entirely self-inflicted. Why don't I just not be like this?' Instead I thought, 'I win again! Take that, established truths of life and work! I operate outside your purview in a zone all of my own! I will never die! More coffee! Why am I sad?!' And thus my academic career continued until I graduated.[93]

This is also why I say I am privileged with an obsessive mind and memory. I could afford, to an extent, to dick around and have these mad compulsions and pathetic, needlessly oppositional behaviours because, ultimately, the smaller amount of time I had for revision or work was still enough to get good grades. If I had the dysfunction but not the obsessiveness and memory, I would not be living the life I am today. Frankly, I would probably be unemployable: no serious qualifications, too easily bored and distracted for many jobs, resentful of a society that never seemed to comprehend my difficulties. I think I know myself well enough to say that, had I not been able to live the life I have, I would be a difficult problem for society to solve.

You might be wondering why I was power-walking, sodden with sweat, from one side of Cambridge to the other,

---

93 To be fair, not *entirely* like that, or I'd have died, but far too often like that. My least insane effort was my dissertation, heavily researched and in my opinion truly inspired. However, even that ended up, in the execution of actually writing it, with me and my friend George staying up for thirty hours straight in the IT room of Homerton College, eating pizza and desperately typing out our first drafts, googling and farting and laughing hysterically with the terrible energy of pure panic.

instead of cycling gracefully like Cambridge students should? Beautifully coasting down medieval streets, gown flapping in the wind, waving cheerfully at vicars? Well, when I arrived at university, I saw my fellow freshers all going and getting bicycles. In Cambridge, you get a bicycle from any of the various independent charming shops that feed the town's insatiable appetite for bicycles. Cambridge is also constantly suffering from an epidemic of bike theft that it is, apparently, impossible to stop, and so demand is infinite.

My new friend George and I reckoned that these bikes were insanely overpriced, partially because I had arrived from the Isle of Man and George from Wolverhampton where, in comparison to Cambridge and the richer south-east of England, prices of anything from bikes to pints were practically pre-war. Thus outraged by Cambridge's prices, we decided we could buy some crappy mass-produced bike from a supermarket and assemble it ourselves. We trudged to the outskirts of Cambridge to the retail park and bought our disassembled bikes, bikes that looked alarmingly like bikes for children. The student bikes at the shops in Cambridge, the ones being purchased by the 'proper' students, were large, noble beasts with thin tyres and delicate frames. Our bikes had fat tyres and childish, chunky frames and came with little lightning-bolt symbols on the box and too many gears. I think the bike was called something like CHAOS LIGHTNING or CRASH SABRE, too. Looking back, our behaviour was like the behaviour of eccentric drunks. Why didn't we just fucking buy normal bikes? What was *wrong* with us?! I can't believe just *how wrong we were*, but at the time we were certain we had seen through the Matrix and that this was a brilliant idea.

WHY CAN'T I GET ANYTHING DONE?

We assembled the bikes in the park, reasoning that it was silly to walk all the way back to our colleges carrying a bike only to assemble it there. I don't know if either of us had assembled something properly before but I doubt it. We did our best with the Allen keys and manuals provided but we were not the kind of people to assemble them properly. I tried riding mine and it was agony. I am an enormous man, it was, frankly, too small. It was as mad as riding a Shetland pony around and the seat dug painfully into my perineum (or 'gooch') to the point where I wouldn't be surprised if I still had CHAOS LIGHTNING imprinted in reverse on my fucking prostate. I wobbled agonisingly home. I tried riding it to lectures *once* and, at a four-way junction, I tried to turn left. The handlebars turned, so points for that, but the wheel did not. Visions flashed before my eyes of my weeping family watching CCTV footage of me driving a bike that was somehow pointing in two directions into oncoming traffic. 'Why didn't he buy a *normal bike?!*' my mother would wail. I recovered and got to the pavement, cars hooting, and walked the twisted beast home in shame. I shackled it to a bike rail in the courtyard of our accommodation and, like an aristocratic family with a mad relation, left it there to rust for the next few years. Every now and then I would remember that it was there and cringe until my skin crumpled.

I spent the next three years of my degree walking all over town, with tens of kilograms of books and laptop, sweating like a pig. Every time people said, 'Wait, why don't you just cycle?'(they said it often), I would snap, 'It's too complicated' and hope to leave it at that. After all, I was busy, wasn't I? I had Danish archaeological terms to guess! But I wasn't too busy. At literally *any* point in those three years I could have got a normal bike. At *any* time. I just *didn't*. For *no* reason. I know that's absolutely insane, but in my head the whole process of buying and riding and owning a bike had already proved beyond me, and that was that. Whenever I considered it, I would think, 'But I already *own* a bike! Oh *God*, that *thing*' and I would be paralysed because: I didn't need to buy a bike because I already had one, except it was an inappropriate bike that didn't work, but that's something I should fix instead of buying a new one, which is even more money than the money I tried to save, but I can't fix it, because even if it worked the bike is shit, so I need a new bike, but I already have a bike, but—' And so it would loop around and around in my head.

As I get older, I am getting much better at saying, 'Fuck it' and taking the shortcut when I can, cutting the looping, negative thoughts that lead to paralysis. But it's not easy, and it still happens.

If you are reading this and sceptical that an autistic person you know has executive dysfunction, consider how much they are instinctively hiding from you! While writing this book, I mentioned my executive dysfunction on a road trip with my friends, the comedians Alex Kealy and Ivo Graham. They expressed both surprise and their sense of me as a very well-put-together, high-functioning person. I then explained to them that if they looked carefully at my hair, they would see I had styled it with pink hand soap from the public toilets before a gig because I had forgotten my hair wax. Also, the McDonald's we'd just stopped to eat at was my fifth disorganised meal of the day. Later, I left half of my laptop charger in Alex's car. I think I convinced them.

Why don't I do things I know I should do?

When I was a teenager, I went through a phase of not washing my hair. I also went through a phase of not brushing my teeth, or not enough or not properly. It's obviously gross, but I knew that it was gross at the time. I knew that I should do these things, that it was bad not to, that it made me look bad, that it made my already bankrupt social life worse, that (in the case of teeth) it would result in genuine issues later, that it was baffling and infuriating to my mum. I knew all of this, I agreed with these statements, and I still deliberately did not do it. I have no idea why.

The mystery of what the hell was wrong with me only deepened the older I got. I would periodically remember that I'd gone through these phases and be completely unable to put myself back in the mindset. '*Why* did I do that?' I'd agonise, lying awake at night. The nearest thing I can compare it to is knowing that you should do some laundry and putting it off, but even that doesn't quite cover it. You'd still end up doing the laundry after one or two weeks, even three, and a pile of laundry isn't physically uncomfortable or socially visible, whereas uncleaned teeth and greasy hair feel awful and look awful. There was no upside and I struggle to think of a downside more visceral and motivating than being unclean and feeling disgusting, so what the *hell* was going on?

So many times in my life I had *felt it* as I sabotage myself through inaction and felt powerless to stop it. Every single time it felt as though I was in a car rolling down a hill towards the sea: no engine, no brakes, just trapped and unable to intervene. Except I was able, I could literally have stopped the car at any time, it was entirely up to me! And I just ... didn't? I wanted to, or felt like I did, I knew I should, I knew I would feel terrible shame or guilt or embarrassment later but I still just ... let it happen. *Why?* What is *wrong* with me?

I'd tried to describe this feeling to people but no one seemed to have a clue what I meant. They'd say it sounded bizarre or crazy or like self-sabotage and I'd say, 'Yes, it is, but *why?*' and they'd be no use. One or two people I met would know what I meant, they'd have it too, but they'd be equally clueless and unsettled. I was always too aware of how odd it was to ever ask a high number of people; I was too aware that 'why do I let things fall apart, even when I don't want to?' sounded like the sort of thing someone would say on an Arctic expedition before they left the tent and calmly disappeared into a blizzard. It was a mystery, until while researching my own diagnosis I heard about 'demand avoidance'.

Demand avoidance means resisting the demands of everyday life in a persistent and notable way. It does not refer to the sort of demand avoidance we all experience when we can't be arsed hoovering, or don't want to go to the gym, or resent being bossed around by someone. When I first came across the phrase 'demand avoidance' I felt an odd feeling creep over me – this sounded like it could be that mysterious thing that I had! Another eerie personal revelation in the legion of revelations from researching autism. I googled it and my blood ran cold to discover that not brushing your teeth, especially when specifically instructed to, was one of the go-to examples. Not only was my shameful problem from my teenage years no longer a mystery, it wasn't even rare: it was the *example*, for God's sake.

I should flag that demand avoidance is a controversial, under-researched area. It has been suggested by experts like Dr Luke Beardon that this avoidant reaction is simply a manifestation of anxiety in autistic individuals as opposed to some sort of deliberate resistance. There isn't a lot of good data and you'll be more likely to find solidarity with your experiences on places like Reddit than some large study that tries to explain it scientifically. Lack of data isn't the only reason it's controversial; it's also due to the potential for bias or misinterpretation. For example, a particularly unsympathetic researcher might characterise an autistic child who refuses to wear correct school uniform as being demand avoidant, or needlessly disobeying a harmless instruction. However, what if the autistic child has a severe sensory issue with the fabric of the uniform but not an issue with the idea of uniform itself? Then their resistance is as justified as a non-autistic person refusing to wear underpants made of sandpaper.

There is also a danger of pathologising resistance to demands and instructions that actually stems from social or political issues. For example, a child from a minority who has experienced discrimination or ill-treatment at the hands of the police might not obey instructions from the police. Or it might be political, like a pacifist refusing to obey military orders. Those examples might sound trite or obvious but they are both situations where, in the past, systems have used accusations of mental illness to stigmatise and delegitimise individual acts of resistance. I have come across the view that all demand avoidance and defiance in autism is a legitimate and understandable reaction to a society and system that generally ignores the needs, desires and autonomy of autistic people throughout their lives, a natural reaction to the trauma of it all. I think there is some truth in that, but having experienced it myself, I don't know if it is *all* that, or even if this sort of soaring rhetoric is of any use when you're a parent trying to stop your kid letting his teeth rot in his mouth for no reason. It's extremely difficult to untangle sensory issues, anxiety, stress and generic childhood rebelliousness.

It is fascinating to go online and dive into the debates and research around exactly how to describe or classify this phenomenon, however I am content to leave that to the experts. The controversy and debates go back forty years and there are new papers being published all the time, so it would take another whole book to properly explain, describe and engage with.

For our purposes, the safest bet is simply to note that 'demand avoidance' of some kind can occur with autism and acknowledge that we should deal with it on a person-by-person basis. For example, I believe that my baffling refusal to brush my teeth was fairly arbitrary demand avoidance – something to do with rebellion maybe, whereas for some autistic people it could be down to a sensory issue with the feeling of bristles on gum, the foaminess or burning sensation of the toothpaste. Their resistance would be a sensory issue, not demand avoidance.

The National Autistic Society website explains that demand avoidance affects direct demands like instructions; internal demands like hunger; and indirect or implied demands such as an electricity bill that needs to be paid.

This tracks with my memories. I can remember resisting the internal demand (brush your teeth, for fuck's sake, it feels horrible) and, whenever my baffled parents said something about brushing my teeth, it would almost always make it worse. I would feel whatever it was stopping me harden, become more determined to never give in and do what was being instructed. Looking back, I can only grasp at possible reasons why. When I was a toddler, I remember hating the taste of toothpaste and found my teeth being brushed by a parent very painful, or at least I remember squirming and complaining a lot. I also utterly loathed my childhood dentist, who to my recollection was extraordinarily rude, patronising and hated waiting for the anaesthetic to kick in, or maybe believed that I was lying to delay her drill, and would forge on regardless. This is all great stuff, in terms of origin stories for 'teenager who hates brushing his teeth', but it doesn't explain the sheer self-sabotage of it. After all, my behaviour was only making my hateful dentist wealthier. It also doesn't explain not washing my hair – I wasn't being mercilessly taunted by a cruel barber, like some character in an opera.

There are a few explanations floating around the internet, such as an autistic need for certainty, or feelings of anxiety, leading to a sort of knee-jerk enforcement of autonomy by the autistic person as a way of reclaiming control. Otherwise, this is one of those areas where even the full weight of the internet cannot help us. If I had to guess, I'd say that my periods of demand avoidance were a combination of childhood resentment of the task itself or some forgotten sensory issue, teenage rebellion and nihilism, a deep need for autonomy (at least I'm filthy on *my terms*), and the anger or irritation of being told how to behave and how to exist building up over many years.

I think there was some self-loathing in there, too, where the lack of personal care was a sort of indirect self-harm, an external, physical sign of how I felt about myself. I was also very resentful of social pressures – *why* did we need to do these things? The second someone said something like 'because you just *do*', I would immediately stop complying with whatever they were describing. As far as I was concerned, if they couldn't justify it to me, they couldn't demand it of me. As you can imagine, this was probably a really fun, relaxing and interesting time for my parents, having to spend half an hour every morning negotiating with a greasy pedant.

Over time, I have largely grown out of this bizarre, difficult behaviour, but part of that is probably the difference in being spoken to like a child and being spoken to like an adult. To this day, if someone offered me ten thousand pounds in a patronising tone, I would have to fight the urge to tell them angrily to fuck off. It is another area where doing army cadets was useful – the instructions were never patronising and they were often to do with pretty important stuff like weapons safety, and you learned that you didn't know best, so the safest thing to do was to follow the instruction and not waste time quibbling. The rest of the change I see in myself is down to having to repeatedly experience the consequences of this behaviour and slowly getting so bored of myself that I eventually forced myself to get over it. I have friends in recovery and some have said similar things about what motivated them to get sober or clean: sometimes it's a dramatic revelation or near-death experience, sometimes you just get so sick of your own behaviour, so exhausted with yourself, that it overrides the power of whatever was inside you that made you behave like that.

CHAPTER 12

Why Don't I Have a Normal Relationship with Food?

When it comes to autism there is a symphony of reasons why you might have an unusual relationship with food. Autism intersects neatly with food issues in areas like compulsion, sensory difficulties, inability to recognise internal feelings, and need for routine or control. Autism and food issues are like burgers and chips. You can have one without the other but it's unusual and I will fear and envy your self-control.

Picky eating

When I was a kid I was a very picky eater. That's not uncommon and not necessarily a sign of neurodivergence, but it depends on the severity and the motivation of the picky eater. For whatever reason, I was very resistant to trying new foods. With autism, your sensory abilities can be heightened, but not in a cool Spider-Man way, more in a burdened-by-power 'I can smell everyone's breath from miles away' way.

My poor, suffering mother tried to convince me to have porridge for breakfast one day when I was maybe four or five. 'Only bears eat porridge,' I said, frowning, and that was that. In my defence, I was only going off the data I had available to me at the time. Did Goldilocks eat porridge? Sure, but only within the larger context of burglary. We can't condone it.

I remember being repeatedly disappointed and sickened by chicken drumsticks. In comic books and cartoons, chicken or turkey drumsticks were the ultimate food. A lovely, clean white cartoon bone with a sort of bum shape on one end and, on the other, a perfect brown oval of Vague Flesh. Cartoon characters would wave these things around, tearing delicious roast hunks off with their teeth or even somehow yanking the whole lump off the bone in one go, leaving a cartoon femur to be thrown over their shoulder. It looked incredible. The closest we have ever come as a species to creating this ultimate food was that upsetting 'chicken bites' trend a few years ago. This was where you could go to a shop and get a small sack of cold, nude nuggets that released a fart when you opened it as a kind of aperitif.

Drumsticks never lived up to their potential. They always looked the part. I'd spy one in the fridge and visions of medieval feasts would dance before my eyes. Once you grasp it, though, it all changes. It's too visceral. The bone isn't white and clean and neatly symmetrical, it's grey and brown and has a nobble of something at the end. The meat doesn't exist as a perfect oval. In fact, the meat is often under a jacket of chicken skin. Obviously, the dream is crispy chicken skin, but so often the cold supermarket drumstick is wearing a greasy robe of bollock leather. Once you undress the drumstick, you're finally face to face with the bit you want to eat but it isn't the glorious brown oval. It's a collage of crescents of meat that are interlocked, all perfect mouthfuls in their own way, sure, but linked by cartilage, like that single thin spine that runs up and into the meat as if to pin it to the mast of the bone. Even once you deal with these and tear the meat off with your teeth, you may end up revealing some unsettlingly purple bits of bone previously hidden from God's sight.

To be clear, I am completely over this now and will gleefully chew through the gristle of chicken wings like a demon. It does mean that I completely understand when other people don't eat meat because they are overwhelmed by a sort of body horror. It's like they see themselves reflected in the cooked meat, subconsciously or consciously. Obviously it's never nice to be reminded that you're essentially an elaborate web of gristle filled with blood and opinions, flapping down the road, listening to music and so on, but it's especially unpleasant to be reminded of this during a meal.

As a child, I was also completely against my food touching. The idea of eating the way I could see adults eat, putting a bit of everything on a fork, was repulsive. Why not smash the Sunday roast into the ice cream and eat everything at once like dog food if you like mixing tastes so much?! I still take issue with some mixing, especially the British obsession with trying to hide sweetcorn in everything – sandwiches, on pizzas, in salads. Repulsive! Sweetcorn is friends with peas because they are the same guy but wearing different coloured jackets, OK? But neither of these sweet little nodules should go anywhere near anything savoury that isn't rice. When I go to Subway, I hate to see a lone sweetcorn abandoned in a tray of other ingredients. A rogue yellow tooth.

I also had issues with leftovers. Once food was finished being food for the first time it was, in my opinion, over. It was horrifying to scrape the (once perfectly separate) food into a Tupperware coffin and smoosh the tepid remains up against each other. The act of reheating was also fraught, a rogue cold area within an otherwise impossibly hot food would revolt me beyond measure, as well as the general flatulent smell of decay when opening a container of leftovers. I did gradually get over this through time and exposure, but I wonder how much of it is down to having particularly sensitive smell or taste.

Being a picky eater makes you something of a pariah. The other kids will regard you as a baby and it can be extremely stressful to go to other people's houses. If their parent or caregiver plops down some mad creation in front of you, or in my case, almost anything touching, you will be torn between forcing yourself to eat something that makes your mind scream or the even greater horror and shame of 'being rude to a mum'. Part of my exposure therapy was deciding that coming across as 'rude' or 'spoilt' was so incredibly shameful, to me and to my parents, that I just had to learn to flick a switch in my head and completely block out the food horror.

The way I created this switch in my head was during a weekend exercise with the cadets on the Isle of Man. I would have been a young teenager at the time. We were camping in the woods and discovered that, after our first night sleeping under ponchos in army sleeping bags, the bitterly cold and overcast night we had patrolled through had become a beautiful snowy morning. A deep blue sky, slate grey sea and white snow hiding the green Manx Hills. All very nice, except for the fact that we had never been so cold in all our lives and had only a few hours of fitful sleep. The tips of our noses were all that had been exposed during the night and they stung like hell – not frostbite, but maybe frostnip. We hopped shivering into the trees and stared enviously at the steam off our morning piss. It was around six in the morning and we needed to warm up, so we lit hexamine fuel blocks in their little stoves and poured water into the mess tins we balanced over the flame. Once the water was boiling, we threw in the tea bags, milk power and sugar, and sat by the little chemical flame with wet gloves and damp boots. I have never wanted a hot drink more in my life. The second it seemed vaguely ready, I reached out for the wire handle of the mess tin to pour it into my metal cup. At that moment, the wind picked up and some dry grass and pine needles pirouetted whimsically right into the tea.

I sat, shivering, and realised that my normal impulse would be to furiously tip the stuff out and abandon the idea. Then again, I *needed* this hot drink. I felt something shift in my brain. It was like a door bolt sliding across or a light turning on. I was exhausted, I was freezing, I was in a rush, and I just thought, 'Oh ... who gives a shit. I don't care anymore.' Then in cheerful surprise, 'Oh! I don't care! It's only grass, and it's still boiling, so that's probably clean. I'll pour it from a corner so the grass doesn't go in my cup. I just won't give a shit *for now*. Normal service will resume shortly.' Ever since that moment I have been able to simply 'switch off' my problem with something, or totally seal off some sensory horror and get on with whatever I am up to.

WHY CAN'T I JUST ENJOY THINGS?

As I grew older, because I felt I had fixed myself,[94] I developed some contempt for picky eaters. We always hate most the things we see in ourselves or have had to change. I remember completely changing my mind when, having lunch with the script genius Andrew Ellard, a picky eater, he described his bafflement at how negatively people reacted to picky eaters in restaurants. 'It doesn't affect your meal at all!' he pointed out. 'And what's the point in going out and paying money to eat at a restaurant if you can't specify what you want?'[95] He was right! Obviously it can still be inconvenient but then so are literally any dietary requirements, right down to preference for spice level, so maybe none of it matters and we can all just agree to cater to each other. After all, it would be an insensitive and disrespectful friend who referred to a religious or medical dietary requirement as 'picky eating', so why not see an internal need the same way?

That is the optimal solution not only because it fosters a mutual compassion that I think would serve society well, but because the solution that worked for me is so impossible to repeat. It is phenomenally demoralising to say to people that the solution is to gradually erode your own desires and needs over time. Especially when, if you are content with your own picky eating and it's not causing health issues, you'd only be going through all that effort to make other people happy. Maybe what worked for me could work for others! Perhaps I could set up a stall in the high street with an enormous banner

---

94 I even now eat and enjoy porridge, though in fairness that has coincided with becoming more bear-like as I've aged.

95 One of the advantages of the flavour of autism I have, at least, is that if someone expresses a perfectly logical point that removes one of my arguments I will, generally, be able to immediately change my mind. It's rarer than you think.

that reads SUFFERING IS THE ANSWER and offer to throw dirt into people's hot drinks? 'This'll *change* your *brain!*' I'd bellow cheerfully, lunging for their takeaway mocha with a fistful of hay.

Need for routine

A lot of people on the spectrum report a desire to eat the same thing over and over again. This is true to the point where the idea of a 'samefood' has become a meme online, describing a specific food that one eats repeatedly, either according to a schedule or for days at a time. I'm more of a schedule person. I don't require variety in my day-to-day life – I'm happy enough with it if someone else is responsible, but I don't need it in my routine. I find that the neurotypical people I know, with their desire for endless food novelty, can seem bizarrely decadent. Oh, would the Sultan prefer a *different* breakfast for the fourth day in a row?

I still enjoy eating nice, varied meals, however, but they need to be what I think of as meals that matter. Breakfast and lunch, especially during the week, do not matter. Every single precious piece of energy that I spend dicking around choosing something for lunch or breakfast is a waste and if forced to make a decision, dear reader, I will be paralysed by choice. Choosing things is exhausting and impossible, especially if I am making something at home and the choices are practically infinite. The sheer range of things one can do with an egg goes from being a positive to a negative. I need to desperately conserve this energy for things that do matter, like relationships and work, and not end up being ill-tempered in some social scenario because I fucked up an omelette I decided to make on a whim.

Meals that matter to me are: meals out with others, or meals on a Friday night or any time on Saturday or Sunday. As far as I am concerned, almost all other meals could be the same thing, as long as they were nutritionally balanced (although this is a recent requirement of mine). Don't get me wrong, I am still quite specific about what the meals that don't matter should be, it's just that I don't care if they're not varied. I have never given enough of a shit about one of these meals to the extent that I was willing to, say, sprinkle some spring onions over them that I have had to purchase and slice myself. It seems like vanity to me, but mainly it's energy I cannot spare. Save it for the weekend! Not every meal is a *MasterChef* final!

This was the good part of eating at school and the university canteen – the same stuff on the same days scheduled over and over. Predictable, reliable, and the range of choices limited to a perfectly reasonable three options. God, I miss eating in institutions. If I could, I would go for breakfast and lunch every weekday in some big warehouse near my flat called THE CANTEEN – plastic trays and everything. All the thinking, all the cooking, all the choice: taken care of! Never mind the washing up. It's probably the most Soviet of my desires and definitely played a role in how appealing I found a potential career in teaching, academia or the military. It's hard to write about this stuff without coming across as a Puritan, some culinary Savonarola demanding that everything delicious and fancy be condemned as decadence and thrown into the bonfire. I'm not! I am a big fan of fancy things that are nice – I just don't *need* them the way some people seem to and, if

I am the one responsible for them, find the choice aspect stressful. Thank God for restaurants.

If your sense of taste and smell are very sensitive then there is an added incentive not to vary your routine. The sheer risk of choosing or making the wrong thing is simply too high to be worth it. Your entire day can be completely ruined (and valuable energy wasted) by choosing something disappointing or unexpectedly time-consuming, so why risk it? Go with the devil you know and you will retain enough energy to pretend to know what people are talking about when you arrive at the office: '*Strictly Come Dancing*? Why, of course! I love the contestants. I watched it, that's for sure, and certainly didn't spend that evening playing a videogame where I used a haunted watch to solve murders on an East India Company ship.'[96]

Full disclosure: after years of field testing various meals, I think I have finally settled upon the breakfast combination that's perfect for me. Every day that I can, I eat toasted rye bread and eggs. I realised that, when it comes to the meals that don't matter, I eat to feel full enough and have enough energy so that I don't get distracted or start eating junk during the day. Eating toasted rye bread is like homework for your mouth – it's good for you but you aren't supposed to *love* it. You do learn to enjoy it though and over time white bread seems more and more like spreading butter on cotton wool. Rye bread is expensive, it turns out, so I genuinely order it in bulk from the internet to save money and because it doesn't go off for months. I admit that 'ordering boxes of special internet

---

96   Return of the Obra Dinn – it's fucking *incredible.*

bread' is one of the most autistic things I do, but it saves me from forgetting to eat an entire loaf before it goes mouldy and being filled with guilt and shame as I bin a load of hairy green bread. Plus, it's high in fibre!

Over- and undereating

This brings us to our old friends, over- and undereating. I choose these slightly vague terms because not all overeating is binge eating and not all undereating is anorexia. In fact, as a part of the larger constant misdiagnosis of female autistics, strong food preferences regarding routine, taste, texture and so on can be misdiagnosed as anorexia when they are just a combination of autistic food preferences and social mirroring, in the case of autistic young women surrounded by anorexic peers. That's not to say that autistic people cannot be anorexic, of course they can. Simply that this is yet *another* area of healthcare that autism makes *even more complicated*. Hooray for layers!

I love to overeat. I have never had an issue with tobacco, drugs or alcohol – I am a big fan of booze but if I am not socialising, I can do without it for weeks. My issue has always been food. I don't think it's a coincidence that I started binge eating or overeating in general during sixth form, when I was extremely stressed by the intensity of the work[97] and I had newly discovered and adopted social masking. I went from a pretty slim kid with big limbs to very chunky indeed. Stretch

---

97 I did the International Baccalaureate because I am an awful, privileged internationalist. It's a hell of a qualification and turned my brain from a lump of pork into a jet engine that fires out essays. Stressful, though!

marks formed a terrible, purple belt all around my waist and I was panicked and ashamed by their appearance. I had never particularly had to think about what I was eating before in terms of energy content – I was always vaguely unfit and asthmatic but never really overweight. Food, you see, was my reward. For years I struggled with the idea that people existed without some sort of reward, or that they saw their own paltry decadences as sufficient reward. Your *reward* is two pieces of bacon and two eggs? *That's* the big prize? I was putting in the hard yards when it came to social behaviours and academics and the one place where I permitted myself indulgence was through food and emotional eating.

Also, our old friend alexithymia makes it difficult to tell the difference between being hungry, being thirsty, being tired and being full. This meant that the only way I could know for sure (and get that lovely 'I am full now' feeling) was to eat to excess. It was also, as any overeater can tell you, a lot of fun. Newsflash: food is nice! Especially the stuff filled with fat, sugar and salt! That's another reason I eat my ridiculous internet bread – if you want to feel full, hoo boy, rye bread is for you. It's also slow-release energy, whereas white bread works for a little while but after an hour or two I crash like a tranquilised buffalo and lust for cornershop treats.

I would say that if I have what they call disordered eating, then binge eating is my disorder. However, I have, like a lot of disordered eaters, gone through periods of excessive dietary control. There are upsides to controlling your diet, obviously. It's easier to be healthy and your tastes change. For example, I was astonished to find that after months of being healthy that the idea of eating a slice of cheap pepperoni pizza, shiny with grease, was gross to me. I would literally never have believed that it was possible. In fact, it was a revelation because of how utterly it undermines the idea of willpower. People go on and on about willpower being the key to healthiness and so I reasoned that everyone I knew had the same insane food desires that I did. Everyone I knew was just as excited by the idea of ordering so much from a takeaway you get a family discount! It's simply that I was weak and these other people were strong! They somehow had the monk-like discipline to ignore and suppress desires that I found overwhelming. I believed this for years and adjusted my self-esteem accordingly. It was a delight in some ways and infuriating in others to discover that these fuckers had never even wanted to eat unhealthily the way I did. It was easy for them not to do the things I did *because they didn't want to do the things I did.* It took no more willpower for them to resist eating an entire pizza than it would take me willpower to resist jamming my thumbs into my eyes. Over time, if you do use the willpower, your tastes will change and you can achieve this lack of desire, but the battle is never truly over.

Sometimes, when I have been particularly fascistic, I have felt the sinister tug of going the other way. I sympathise with undereaters and anorexics. I have felt the incredible panic and shame of knowing that you've gone over your 'calorie allowance', even though you've been strict for weeks and it doesn't matter. I've felt the headrush of pride and achievement when turning down a dessert, or booze, or having salad instead of fries. A little tickle that says go for it, do more, turn down more, let's get *obsessed.* The feeling, when you see in the mirror that you have changed and feel looseness in your clothes, that at *last* you have power and control over *something!* Not just anything, your *own* physical form, like some sexy shapeshifter! It's certainly intoxicating. An old friend of mine ended up working at a clinic that treated, among other things, eating disorders and told me that the men who get booked in don't starve or undereat at the same rate as the female patients, because the male body ideal often involves muscle growth. There are male anorexics but more common is steroid abuse, compulsive exercise, only eating protein and suchlike. That might be what always saved me from following the dark thrill of restriction – even during my more dramatic bouts of weight loss, I would only restrict calories up to a point, as I was still interested in being physically strong. I would still be very tired or hungry in the evenings and probably going too far, but I can't claim to have been in any danger. A lot of it was definitely autistic obsessiveness, routine and control – finally, a way to formalise my desire for things to be the same and known. I cannot tell you how soothing it is to know what you're going to have most days and not have to think about it. It's the dietary version of Steve Jobs wearing the same clothes every day.[98]

If this all sounds crazy to you, that's fine. You only need to understand something very simple: autistic person finds X to be stressful, solution Y removes the stress. That's it – that's the entire equation you need to know to remove any of your confusion around why anyone would do Y. You don't actually need to understand it on a gut level, you just need to accept that it is true for the person telling you.

---

98   Different sets of clothes, I mean. He wasn't that crazy. Well, not in that specific way.

WHY CAN'T I JUST ENJOY THINGS?

If you're reading this and are autistic or suspect that you could be, it might be the first time you've thought of your food issues as part of autism and not a separate matter. That's part of the appeal of the diagnosis for me, the fact that such a wide range of daily difficulties can be explained by a condition. It means that you can approach the situation from a 'being autistic' angle and work on it that way, as opposed to being endlessly redirected to resources, advice and assistance designed for someone with a completely different neurotype. I always found the advice and approach from GPs on my dietary issues either useless or baffling or both, but now that I can look up the perspectives of fellow autistic people or advice from professionals directed at autistic people specifically, it's made a huge difference. It's hard accepting that autism means it might be an 'all my life' problem though, but that's the truth, and I'm getting over my frustration at that slowly but surely. Full disclosure, I am writing this eating a mince pie.

CHAPTER 13

Autistic Burnout

We've all heard the word burnout. I seem to hear it most often in the media to describe either the creative burnout of authors who never write enough to satisfy their fans, or to describe famous people who live in California and are either genuinely burned out from running a robot company/harvesting our data/being an actor, or their publicist has advised them that burnout from sheer hard work plays better than 'currently in rehab'. That's not to say rehab and burnout don't go hand in hand, they do. It's just that I think the way we use the word burnout in day-to-day language has trained us to have a more flippant attitude to it than it deserves. In the past, I would have presumed that autistic burnout was similar to everyday casual burnout – bad, but a week or two off and you'll be fine. I was wrong!

Autistic burnout is a natural (autistic) response to stressful circumstances. It is profound mental, physical or emotional exhaustion. Crucially, it is distinct from neurotypical burnout and from depression. Some of the signs of autistic burnout are: pervasive or chronic fatigue, increase in meltdowns or shutdowns, greater irritability, an increase in sensory sensitivity, physical pain, headaches, worse executive functioning and a loss of skills, which is to say social skills but also even skills like drawing. These can lead to depression and then the burnout and depression can lead to suicidality. It's all bad news, I'm afraid. No autistic superpowers here! You can't get so completely burned out that you, I don't know, get really good at coding or something.

To give some personal examples, when I am burned out I am far more sensitive to noises that normally irritate me a little. If I am rested and functioning, I can bear a certain amount of open-mouth chewing. If I am burned out, I have genuinely had to stop myself walking over to people's tables in restaurants or on trains and asking them to chew with their mouths closed. One day, I will probably snap and do it, and it will go really badly. Or worse – it will work! It will work because I am a very large, bearded man and I will become addicted to the power of fear. Eventually, Batman will have to step in.

When I am burned out, I lose my ability to make jokes or be much fun. I feel like nothing is occurring to me, my mind is drawing a blank and all I can do is acknowledge things, say yes or no, 'that is good' or 'that is bad'. Everything feels like it is happening underwater. My face stops expressing how I am feeling as much as it used to. Talking feels impossible and when I do talk, I think I am speaking normally but often I am barely audible. I then have to repeat myself several times, gradually getting louder each time, as in the past I have accidentally gone straight from barely audible to sudden bellowing and it scares the shit out of people. Like when you watch television and the actual show dialogue is mumbling but the second it goes to adverts you have to leap onto the remote like a grenade because it's like God Himself is screaming at you about home insurance. In this respect, burnout is very similar to an autistic shutdown, but it isn't happening in response to an immediate trigger like a very dramatic, emotional conversation. It's happening in response to sustained stress over time and could last days or weeks.

I feel a need to rest my entire brain the way that you'd rest a muscle and even the strain of watching the stupidest bollocks possible on Netflix is too much to ask. My memory becomes bad and I forget things that normally would spring to mind easily. I can't even do things that I enjoy normally. Judging by some of the accounts of autistic burnout online, there's a good chance you'll suffer from chronic exhaustion.

Executive function also takes a general hit. I was once burned out but still trying to do gigs all over the place and ended up leaving my possessions scattered across the country like someone setting up a treasure hunt. A laptop charger to a budget hotel in Leeds, my electric toothbrush in Bristol and show merchandise in Edinburgh.

Self-care takes a hit. I won't have the energy for exercise, for example, and some people find it very difficult to shower or take much care of their appearance. When burned out, I definitely dress more like someone with a terrible hangover – no jeans, belts or tight shoes, all the clothes are low-effort, unrestricting and soft. This could also be down to increased sensory problems that make restrictive clothes or clothes with too many layers intolerable.

My diet goes nuts, too. Not literally – that sounds healthy. I suppose literally my diet goes fats. I mentioned it being like a hangover above and I think you could do worse for an analogy for burnout than to see it as being hungover for months. Maybe not the immediate nausea and headache part but definitely the *afternoon* section of the hangover, exhausted – a need for comfort, anxiety about everyday things and, of course, junk food. If Henry VIII was from Texas, he would eat like me during burnout. A big part of it is the need for energy – you are exhausted and need energy, so you drink energy drinks or coffee and eat calorie-dense foods. It's largely comfort or stress eating and trying to cut down on thinking. During the later stages of one of my national tours, I began to eat chocolate bars and down very strong instant black coffee backstage minutes before going on to ensure that I got a caffeine/sugar rush in time to boost my performance and general vibe. Even the adrenaline rush of performing for hundreds of people is sometimes not enough to snap you out of zombie mode.

When I'm burnt out, I find it far more difficult to cook for myself beyond a limited range of things that are easy to make and vaguely healthy. These are meals that I have invented to replace my original dietary reaction to burnout – cheap takeaway food and oven meals. I remember I got obsessed with planning out the healthiest *and* easiest possible two or three meals I could have every day, purely to cut down on the physical effort of cooking and the abstract effort of thinking and deciding on ingredients. If you suffer burnout, I highly recommend having these plans ready, unless you want to be like me and intermittently put on 6–12 kilograms (one or two stone) in a month of frenzied exhaustion. Think of it like when Jason Bourne goes into those shipping crates and he's got a box full of different passports, currencies and pistols, except in this version he's got a shipping crate full of noodles, stir-fry vegetable mix and sliced chicken.

If you imagine experiencing all of this at once, never mind experiencing it without knowing what's going on or maybe with an unsympathetic family or workplace, it should not be surprising that it can *lead to* depression and anxiety. When it's happening, it feels like it might never stop and that this is your new reality. The fear of being trapped in burnout forever is a big part of what can push autistic people towards suicidal thoughts. This is especially true if the burnout leads to the breakdown of personal relationships, losing a job, losing a hobby, the loss of self-esteem from being unable to take care of yourself (food, hygiene, appearance) as well as the general unpleasantness of being unable to take care of yourself. The exact figures vary but studies consistently show autistic people are at a significantly increased risk of suicidal thoughts and attempts.

Suicidal thoughts may also crop up more often in the autistic population because they suggest a brutally logical and rigid 'solution'. An autistic way of thinking would be: it is *technically* correct that, if you followed through on these thoughts, the problems would *technically* end. Problem: I feel bad due to a set of pervasive and seemingly intractable problems in my life and cannot imagine them ever being solved. Solution: well, I mean I *could* ... Autistic people are prone to using a pure form of logic to twist themselves into dramatic decisions. It's also why we can be prone to being manipulated by others through logic.

To give a less dramatic example, I found it exhausting to constantly open and close the dishwasher and pull out the trays and stack individual cups, cutlery, plates etc. I didn't like all that bending over, and throughout the day the gradual addition of newly dirty cutlery or crockery would necessitate changing the organisation of the dishwasher to accommodate its new guests. To save time and effort, I would stack dirty crockery and cutlery on the sink above the dishwasher and load it all in one consolidated effort at the end of every day before I went to bed. I preferred this because I had no emotional reaction to the sight of a pile of dirty plates that I knew would be cleaned soon enough.

To give a more dramatic example, I once used pure logic to convince myself that it was a good idea to end a relationship at university because I was feeling utterly overwhelmed by life and the relationship was the only non-compulsory part of my life. My logic was flawless but didn't take into account the massive benefits of being in a relationship because I was overwhelmed by stress and couldn't perceive them properly. A lot of autistic people make the mistake of presuming that their *ability* to apply pure logic means that their *perspective* encompasses all points of information needed to feed into that logic. This is not to say that autistic people *don't* get suicidal in the neurotypical way due to depression or distress or terminal illness or whatever, simply that there is an additional pitfall for autistic people to be aware of. It's also good to be aware of these flawed logic spirals if you are the loved one or friend of an autistic person as sometimes the logic can be so convincingly argued that it hooks in people around them. At the same time as being aware of that, please don't use this as a way to dismiss their concerns! Welcome to the tightrope!

Trickily, while suicidal thoughts can be a part of burnout and the autistic population is between three and nine times more likely to consider, plan for or attempt to kill themselves than the general population,[99] a lot of autistic people are described as having suicidal thoughts by clinicians who are not phrasing their questions literally enough. Clinicians might ask, 'Have you thought about suicide?' but I would understand this as, 'Have you thought *about* suicide?' as in 'Have you thought *about* the Second World War?' – of course someone may have thought *about* it. Do you mean 'Have they *considered* it?' Do you mean 'Have they *found it appealing as a course of action?*' Then their answer becomes no. Good old autism, always keeps you guessing.

What causes burnout

The precise causes of burnout will differ from person to person – what burns out a nurse is not what burns out an accountant. However, autistic burnout is broadly due to attempting to function as an autistic person in a non-autistic

99   Newell, V., Phillips, L. and Jones, C. *et al.* (2023). 'A systematic review and meta-analysis of suicidality in autistic and possibly autistic people without co-occurring intellectual disability'. *Molecular Autism* 14, 12. https://DOI.org/10.1186/s13229-023-00544-7

Hedley, D. and Uljarević, M. (2018). 'Systematic Review of Suicide in Autism Spectrum Disorder: Current Trends and Implications'. *Curr Dev Disord Rep* 5, 65–76. https://DOI.org/10.1007/s40474-018-0133-6Kõlves K, Fitzgerald C, Nordentoft M, Wood SJ, Erlangsen, A. (2021). 'Assessment of Suicidal Behaviors Among Individuals With Autism Spectrum Disorder in Denmark'. *JAMA Netw Open.* 4(1):e2033565. DOI:10.1001/jamanetworkopen.2020.33565

world. The chronic stress of trying to function in a way that your autism does not naturally allow you to function and the stress caused by a mismatch of expectations and abilities. The causes may be harder to spot or predict due to the specific problems an autistic person has versus a non-autistic person.

For example, autistic masking. Hiding your autism takes a lot of energy. Let's say you work in an office and are already using the normal amount of energy that it takes to do your job, be on time, be professional. Now, let's take into account the energy you are using:

- To ignore the irritating music or radio shows that people play during the day, because your boss thinks headphones are 'antisocial'.
- To suppress your discomfort and horror at the professional work clothes you have to wear – for example, trying not to think about the fact that your tie makes you feel like you are choking.
- To make enough eye contact to seem normal and sociable but not *too much* either or with the wrong people, a fine line which requires constant thinking or planning.
- Suppressing your urge to stim, whatever that stimming may be. It might be best understood as having a really itchy scalp and being socially unable to scratch it for the entire day.
- Getting anxious over not being in control of your routine, being misunderstood and general anxiety over whether or not your desperate attempts to seem normal are working. Maybe best understood as being

an undercover investigator trying not to get found out.

- Remembering all of the 'correct' ways to make small talk with non-autistic people. For example, remembering that if someone you work with has had a child recently, it is acceptable to ask about the length, weight and name of the child, maybe the length of the labour. However, it is unacceptable to ask, say, if the person involved found the whole thing horrifying or, if they voluntarily did it without pain-relief. You can't pull a baffled face and say, 'Oh *God*, why?!' You have to smile and say something about 'natural' or 'brave', maybe? I genuinely don't know. Even as I am writing this the situation I have just made up has stressed me out.
- Dealing with the lack of understanding or compassion even when you, the autistic person, explain your needs.

The lack of understanding can be a particularly big factor in burnout. Your boss won't let you wear headphones because they are anti-social and they like to imagine their workplace is social, or because then everyone will wear headphones, or because they won't be able to know what you are listening to. This sort of thing means that even after you snap and admit that you need help, you may not only be refused any form of help, you will have your requests held against you as examples of negative character traits. You may end up feeling that you are facing your difficulties completely alone. However, if you try to tough it out and snap later and blame a lack of accommodations, you may be told, 'Well, you never asked,' so there is a catch-22 here.

The paralysing nature of this paradox and the demoralising and isolating effect of being misunderstood, undermined or ignored will pile more stress onto the pre-existing stresses outlined above. There is always a chance that your boss will be understanding, of course, but how to be sure before you ask? That's another drain on your energy – conducting some casual sociological assessment of your employer's views and humanity. All of this is, of course, in addition to any energy you use or stress you experience from simply doing the job like anyone else. After several years of this, what autistic person wouldn't burn out?

Lack of understanding can also be private or social too, of course, not just a workplace issue. If you are undiagnosed or your partner is poorly informed on autism, it could be almost impossible to explain any of the above without seeming completely mad. When you tell your partner that your tie makes you feel like you are choking, if they are non-autistic they will often presume you are speaking metaphorically or that this is a result of a delusion as opposed to a different sensory system. If you explain that you're exhausted from work and hate small talk, they will empathise on the basis that these are common, even utterly generic, complaints for much of the population without comprehending the depth of your problem. This lack of comprehension is the mirror image of our autistic incomprehension that they are *fine* with these things, so it is forgivable, especially if they don't understand autism or you are not diagnosed. However, if they are informed on autism and continue to disbelieve you, play your issues down and fail to understand you – well, it's certainly not going to *reduce* your stress and anxiety.

You may also feel like you are unable to take a break and relax or that taking a break is utterly pointless. Let's imagine that you are the hypothetical autistic office worker described above. How can you take a break when the thing that is driving you mad is not only your job, as in your actual *tasks and work*, but the *environment* of your job and the expectations of society? You know that the environment of your job won't change, never mind *all of society*, so how precisely will you be taking a break? Going full Unabomber and living in a wooden cabin? For how long? There is also the fear that the break will be permanent. What if the break is what ruins the life you've worked so hard to build? Even if it's not permanent, there's a fear that you might get 'out of practice' with masking, start to be yourself, and that this would make it harder to go back to work and even create risks – what if you forget yourself? What if your boss semi-jokingly says, 'Glad to be back?' and you look at him blankly and say, 'No?' Oh *God*.

People pleasing

You may also burn out due to being unable to say no to people or maintaining poor boundaries. Autistic people often respond to the years of rejection they have experienced by becoming 'people-pleasers'. This is not only out of fear of experiencing rejection once again but also possibly due to developing an extreme and unhelpful sense of empathy with the person they should be rejecting, and a corresponding unwillingness to make that person feel the way that they themselves would hate to feel.

I have agreed to *so many* things in my life out of a desire not to make the other person in the situation feel rejected or dismissed. This can cause issues in your relationship with your partner when they realise that you have seemingly devoted four days out of seven to socialising with an insanely wide range of people that they might never even have met. You spend all your energy masking or similar during these and have none left for your homelife, so your partner only gets to experience exhausted, burned-out versions of you. This is not to say that you should mask around your partner too, that would be hell. It's just that it's considerate to save some of that vital energy for your loved ones and not spaff it all on talking to strangers about their new car.

Big changes can cause a huge amount of stress. Changes like a new job, moving house, the end of a relationship, bereavement or even graduating high school. Sometimes, the myriad tasks associated with life changes can paralyse you completely. For example, I once moved from one area of London to another and failed to register with a new GP for three years. If you changed jobs, you might get burned out from having to switch to a different lunch routine, or maybe your new job has some policy on eating at your desk or no microwave in the break room. Small things that can be as exhausting as, say, having to change your phone number across all of your social and professional life.

When I went to university, I initially flourished but by the second year, the lack of structure had begun to drive me mad. I couldn't force myself to attend crucial seminars because of the exhaustion of what in hindsight looks like burnout, and the lack of consequences (detention or whatever) meant it was never a direct problem. Socially, I spent a lot of time in my room – my college friends thought I was hanging out with the comedy/drama freaks and the comedy/drama freaks thought I was hanging out with my college friends. What I was actually doing was haunting my bedroom, exhausted, and largely only doing things late at night like a vampire. My coping skills, developed at high school over a seven-year period, no longer worked in this new environment and I was rapidly trying to build a new system for surviving university life.

This is yet another benefit to being diagnosed. If you are not diagnosed or informed on this stuff, you won't be able to help yourself, much less receive help from others. You won't be able to take a break or avoid burnout if you don't even understand what is causing it or where the problems are arising from. You certainly won't be able to explain your problems to a potentially sympathetic boss or partner without diagnosis and some personal research. How can you take a break from a stressor if you don't even know what it is and why it is stressing you out?

What's unique about autistic burnout?

Autistic burnout is, frankly, weird and a little sinister. It is only recently that the medical establishment has begun to take autistic burnout more seriously. The change came from the sheer number of burnout stories from autistic people online and how incredibly similar they all were. In the past, for this to be taken seriously by the medical establishment, a specific psychologist or team of psychologists would have to take an autistic person seriously when they described burnout. Then they would have to take several more autistic people seriously when *they* described it, and then they would have to decide this pattern was something worth looking into, because what if autistic burnout was its own thing and distinct from neurotypical burnout and other conditions like depression? Then they would have to have proved this using studies and somehow find not only loads of autistic people to join the study, but also a sufficient number that had experienced burnout. *Then* they would have to get this study published and accepted by all the other, presumably sceptical, authorities in the field.

Years would pass and, over time, it might become an accepted phenomenon. This is a strict and reliable way of making sure that most things that 'get through' are scientifically true, but not that most things that are scientifically true 'get through'. Unfortunately, this means that autistic burnout is not in the DSM-5! That's how hot off the presses it is, so you may encounter clinicians who are reluctant to describe your situation as autistic burnout.

Luckily, the internet exists and it's absolutely rammo'd with autistic people. It's given autistic people a chance to compare notes, share life experience and swap advice, and it has concentrated autistic people in a way that is more observable to the medical establishment at the same time that the medical establishment has realised that it might be useful to listen to them.

This has given us the chance to confirm some of the weirder and more sinister aspects of autistic burnout. For example, when I say that autistic burnout can come with a 'loss of skills', I mean that very literally. Go on Reddit or any other autistic forums and you'll read the personal testimonies of people who, after their burnout, were no longer able to draw, having done art for years as a hobby, or had forgotten how to code or how to bake. I mean to say they lost these skills despite them being hobbies and not jobs. As opposed to, say, one Reddit user experiencing autistic burnout lost their photography skills despite being a professional photographer. Any job is a job you can get sick of. That is still burnout and loss of skill, but I think it's murkier if it is also your job, as that could be burnout from the job too, and rejection of the pressure of making money doing photography jobs you don't enjoy.

My point is more that, in terms of painting, baking, coding, these skills were erased from these people's minds even though they were just something they did *for fun and to relax.* They lost the ability to do something fun and relaxing, often *in addition* to burnout removing or reducing their ability to go to work. Neurotypical people seem to deal with burnout by removing work stress and instead doing something they enjoy and that relaxes them. With autistic burnout, there can be skill loss that means you sort of don't even remember *how* to do the fun and relaxing thing. It's like you never knew in the first place but you have all these recent memories of being able to do it. It's bizarre – it would make sense if you didn't go to the gym for five years and then went and discovered that you were unfit. That it was impossible to lift weights as heavy, or run as fast as you did five years ago. Imagine that happening within a month or two *without even having taken a break from the gym.* That's what I find so weird and sinister, it's like the brain erasing a part of its hard drive due to stress. What's worse is that it's erasing a fun, nice, useful bit that could solve the stress!

This is also what differentiates it from depression. Autistic burnout is often mistaken for depression, especially if the person is an undiagnosed autistic or if the clinician is not sufficiently aware of autistic burnout as a distinct phenomenon. To complicate things further, autistic burnout can *lead* to depression and then you have both.

Burnout vs depression

I have experienced burnout and depression and, personally, the difference is best described as follows. So, as I've said, I love videogames. I've always loved them and I play them to destress and give my mind a break. When I was depressed, I found that I no longer felt any desire to play videogames. My mindset was a depressive 'what's the point of even playing them?' attitude. When I am burned out, I *still want to play them* but I *can't*. I am desperate to play them! I can feel how much I need the destressing effect they have on me, I can feel how much I need to escape from my own brain for a while, but it doesn't work. I load up the games but they don't make me feel excited or satisfied when I do well, I am bad at them, my fingers don't seem to know what they are doing anymore, I get frustrated far more quickly. I feel exhausted but also like I want to play them for hours instead of sleeping. I feel furious that the effect I want isn't happening, like someone being given a sugar pill instead of a real drug. When I felt depressed, I wouldn't even bother loading up a game, it was completely unappealing to me.

It might seem subtle but it is an important distinction to bear in mind. In a sick, ironic twist, a lot of the treatment recommendations for depression are things that will make burnout *worse*. At least, initially. For example, if you are depressed, it will almost certainly make you feel better to get some exercise. If you are burned out, you are exhausted and low in energy. Suddenly adding an exercise routine to your stressors could make everything worse.

If you are depressed, you may end up isolating yourself from your social group and loved ones, spending too much time alone or staying in bed in the dark, and this might make depression worse. If you are burned out, there is a high chance you are burned out from socialising and masking your autism, as well as maybe sensory overwhelm. The *solution* to this is less socialising, *more* time alone and, in the sensory overwhelm scenario, more time in dark rooms or away from stimulation. You're also exhausted and will need more sleep than normal, so spending more time in bed could be crucial. Think of it less in terms of how it seems similar to depression and more like a person instinctively trying to create a sensory deprivation tank for themselves.

It's easy to see how someone with burnout that is mistaken for depression could be told to go out *more*, see *more* people and mask even *more*, get even more stimulation, and burn out even harder in a terrible loop where they are constantly pouring petrol on a fire to put it out. There's also a risk of being prescribed antidepressants when they are not fully necessary – after all, an antidepressant will not solve your overwhelming sensory sensitivity.

How to deal with burnout

Because autism is a fickle god, it might seem like I am about to contradict the advice above about not treating it like depression, but remember I said that it would make your burnout worse *initially*. It appears that all the usual things that help depression will also help burnout *once you have the energy to do them*.

We're talking the classics: exercising, getting enough sleep, eating well, doing things that make you happy. However, if you force yourself to start running a 5k every couple of days, get incredibly stressed and anxious about how much sleep you aren't getting and start neurotically planning your diet, you are going to make burnout worse. You will need to rest until you feel reasonably able to incorporate these things into your life again and that rest might take a week of sleeping and lying down in a dark room. It could take weeks or months, it's entirely down to the individual. Some people end up changing careers.

All of this is very intimidating and believe me, I cannot take my own advice. The idea of resting and doing 'light duties' for a month sounds like heaven to me, but then when I think about the practicality of it, I am filled with dread. Not just because turning down work as a freelancer feels like destroying a sandcastle I've spent over a decade building but also because some of the things I'd turn down would not seem like hard work to the people involved and it might not seem healthy to those who don't understand. The problem of perception will come up.

Other non-autistic people *might* accept that you need rest.

However, they may not accept how *long* you need rest for. They will (reasonably, from their perspective) worry that this amount of rest indicates depression or that the resting *is* the breakdown, as opposed to what is fixing the breakdown. They might also, once you have rested and regained your energy, have an issue with you doing things that make you happy. Non-autistic people would more easily accept you going on a ten-day bender in Ibiza as part of your recovery than you asking for time alone to play Minecraft for ten hours. It's odd how, at least in the UK, people will nod benignly, even approvingly, when you describe how you drank so much booze that your sweat smelled like gin, but if you spend a weekend playing hours and hours of Truck Simulator you're a danger to society.

This brings us to our old friend self-advocacy. You're going to have to advocate strongly for your own interests. I was surprised at how strongly some chilled-out people I know resisted autistic points of view when it came down to it – if something doesn't make sense to someone on a *gut* level, on a neurological level, they will take some convincing. Don't charge in there like an FBI agent taking over a crime scene, try to initially start with a gentle but firm explanation and escalate from there as necessary. You'll have to set new boundaries and expectations with the people in your life. Try to find a way that both parties can cooperate to make this work instead of using demands or ultimatums. That's going to be a tough urge to resist after a lifetime of (from your autistic point of view) doing nothing but what everyone else wants to do, masking your true self and ignoring your needs, but you catch more neurotypical flies with honey than with vinegar.

You're going to have to at least *seem* calm and reasonable

when people question your new boundaries and expectations, and they will question them. You've also got to have an action plan for when those boundaries are inevitably crossed which, even if only statistically, you need to accept *will happen.* That's not necessarily because you're autistic and therefore in this minority. Of course, it might be! If it's someone you know to be a bully and a shit, then go on that, hey, it's your life. However, it's important to guard against jumping to feeling victimised in every scenario across all areas of life. It's more likely down to good old human error. People fuck up *constantly* when it comes to treating each other well, autistic or non-autistic, so it happening to you is the most common thing in the world (unfortunately).

Here are a couple of examples from my own life where I tried to address autistic problems that I had with people in my life that, frankly, seem objectively pathetic. (This is another barrier to happiness, an awareness that something causing you huge discomfort seems ridiculous in the grand scheme of things. That awareness of the ridiculousness of your problem does *nothing* to reduce the amount that it bothers you. You might feel ridiculous for having a crippling phobia of spiders but knowing how ridiculous you seem isn't going to help you.)

So, I live with my partner of three years; she moved in after a year and a bit. This felt like a big step, even though it was before my diagnosis, as I knew how exhausted and overexposed I can be with people, even with flatmates. That's easier, of course, because flatmates aren't also in *your* room and *your* bed, but it was what I wanted and I'd never lived with a partner, so I figured it should happen and resolved to do my best.

Now, I have lots of misophonia-based sensory issues and one of those is the sound of cutlery on teeth. I described it already in the sensory issues chapter but suffice to say it makes me want to set my head on fire. I'm afraid my partner, upon moving in, was regularly clacking cutlery on enamel like an old Cockney playing the spoons. That was a problem that I had. She had a problem because I didn't see the point in making the bed. It has long been my view that, if we're talking a mattress and duvet situation, making the bed is faintly ridiculous. All you're doing is smoothing out a thick, billowy duvet so that its shape vaguely matches the shape of the mattress. If we were talking sheets and blankets, like some Second World War hospital or a hotel, sure, that makes sense. Sheets and blankets look and feel awful all tangled up and messy. But it felt to me the entire point of a duvet was to render this sort of old-fashioned labour unnecessary. My partner truly hated the unmade bed. It made her sad and she associated it with illness or depression or disorganisation. Clearly, to her, the unmade bed was a sign of a sinful household and only one step before rolling drunk in the gutter with the dogs and cats of the town.

I proposed a deal. If she would try not to clack cutlery against her teeth ever again, I would make the bed every day. Even though I didn't understand her bed-making argument on a *gut* level, I agreed because it was only fair. After all, she didn't understand *my* cutlery on teeth argument on a gut level either. It's hilarious to me that this deal was drawn up and signed when I was not diagnosed as autistic. I mean, come on. Anyway, this is a good example of setting a boundary or an expectation. In an ideal world, of course, we would both have simply done these nice things for each other, but it was easier to formulate as a kind of deal since it solved two daily irritations for both of us and the end result is the same. I don't mind the bed-making in itself – after all, I enjoy clearly laid-out rules, routines and boundaries. I just don't necessarily see the logic of it and would on my own probably reject it on the basis that the effort it takes is greater than the extra high I get from making the bed and climbing into it later on. However, it is a small price to pay to avoid the agony I feel when I hear someone bite their fork. I have left entire buildings to avoid that sound. An important part of this bargain is accepting the fact that, inevitably, my partner will accidentally or forgetfully clack the cutlery at some point, but that's fine and doesn't have to represent the crumbling of some great treaty. Sometimes even the simple knowledge that a person is trying and that someone is taking you into account *at all* can make all the difference.

On that note, acceptance of your autism and autistic needs will play a huge role in preventing burnout and getting over burnout. Even if a colleague or a loved one isn't very good at it, the fact that they are trying should count for a lot and should reduce the stress and isolation that might have led to the burnout in the first place. Especially if you are late-diagnosed and have spent years being disbelieved or not being taken fully seriously when you did unmask.

It also helps if you have friends who are autistic. We do seem to clump together socially – pre-diagnosis I had three autistic friends and since being diagnosed another friend has been diagnosed and three more are probable candidates. If you haven't customised your life to include as many whackos as possible like I have, then I recommend going online. I've found a lot of the posts on Reddit and other forums and websites incredibly validating and fascinating too. Sometimes you will see someone openly asking about a problem that you've barely been able to formulate the words to describe and some huge puzzle piece will click into place in your mind. It can be nice to have all the camaraderie and validation of reading or adding to these posts along with the distance and convenience of it being text only, anonymous and on your phone. It would be far more of a social effort to physically attend a support group and have to befriend everyone and all open up gradually over time. Exhausting!

If possible, reduce the amount of masking you are doing. Give yourself permission to stim or be weird or play the same song a hundred times or lie in the dark watching yodelling tutorials. Try to reduce the amount of energy you have been spending on hiding who you really are. I acknowledge that this is privileged advice, and you may have a private and/or professional life that makes de-masking difficult or even risky for you, but if you don't manage it somehow you will just burn out again. It's a balance. For example, I have largely stopped trying to talk during, or add to, group conversations where I have nothing to say. In the past I'd have done my best to muck in, throw in some platitudes and do a lot of nodding, but now I am happier having given myself permission to sit quietly and wait for the storm to pass. It's a small thing but it's *such* a relief when it happens.

If you're an anxious, people-pleasing autistic person like me, take more breaks from social activity if you can. It will tear you apart to turn down social invites that you spent your childhood or teenage years craving, but it must be done.

As adults, you don't need as much maintenance time on those friendships and you'd be surprised how fine people are with you cancelling or delaying hanging out. We're all busy! Try not to get stressed about it or you're simply adding to the burnout.

If you are late-diagnosed, non-diagnosed or soon-to-be-diagnosed, you will need to work on your self-knowledge. Learning what works for you is tough, especially if you are autistic. It is the product of listening to yourself and your body over long periods of time and keeping track of what works for you and what fucks you up. Obviously, thanks to poor interoception and alexithymia, 'listening to your body' is not possible for some of us. When I listen to my body, it's in the same way that I can listen to a podcast playing on someone else's headphones sitting across from me, faint and useless.

However, if you use tracking methods, keep a diary, look for patterns in your own vibes and you'll be able to better predict burnout and take preventative measures. It's exactly like working to prevent meltdowns or shutdowns but on a more macro, long-term level. Something that triggers a meltdown or shutdown is in the immediate environment generally over a short period of time, hours or days, but with burnout you should be tracking things over weeks, months, years even. For example, I am aware that I will be spending the entire month of August in Edinburgh, performing at the Fringe, so I can keep an eye on myself and try to have the self-discipline not to add to that burden. If someone asks me to do something during or just before August, I find it a lot easier to say no, now that I have a better sense of what leads to burnout and how important self-advocacy is. Before, I would feel a terrible guilt and probably agree and suffer what I must.

AUTISTIC BURNOUT

If your life is inherently burning you out, either establish sufficient coping mechanisms to compensate or make some changes, because it's going to end in burnout at some stage if you don't. Once you're burned out, the burnout is going to be forcing changes in your life and those changes might be worse and more dramatic than the ones you were putting off due to fear. Get diagnosed, do the research, know thyself, advocate for yourself.

CHAPTER 14

Relationships

I will admit that, certainly compared to what I have seen online, I have had a pretty rosy time during my diagnosis and afterwards. There have been difficulties and revelations aplenty, sure, but compared to some of the heart-breaking stuff you find online I have had a pretty jaunty stroll through autism park.

However, something that I admit got to me is just how many relationship difficulties the condition appears to create. When I got diagnosed, all sorts of relationship difficulties I'd had in the past began to make sense. However, an explanation is not a solution. In fact, there can't really be a solution if the problem is 'I am autistic'. That is unchangeable, after all, but this makes the case for diagnosis: when you know who you are, so too can your partner.

This became apparent when, in an attempt to learn from my autistic brethren, I tried to search the internet for advice on being an autistic man going out with a neurotypical woman. In terms of articles on websites, I found nothing. In fact, there was worse than nothing. What I found was page after page of articles, websites, listicles, you name it, dedicated to helping neurotypical women through the agony and misery of going out with an autistic man. It was demoralising scrolling through page after page of articles asking: 'Is your relationship failing because he is autistic?' Or devastating forum posts and agony aunt columns from women saying that, despite their best efforts, dating, marrying or even having kids with an autistic man had completely destroyed their lives, eroded their mental health and resulted in them feeling crushed by loneliness. A few more pages about 'how to get him to get tested for autism' and inquiries from women trying to figure out how to encourage their clearly autistic partner to get some sort of professional diagnosis, if only to convince them via medical authority that their behaviour was abnormal.

In fairness, a lot of the advice was kind and wise. All sorts of things about patience, kindness, empathy and so on. The harrowing stuff was, in fairness, overwhelmingly from an older generation, where the men (autistic or otherwise) were utterly against any form of self-analysis or improvement and the women utterly against anything that didn't match pre-conceived social norms.

I admit it was interesting reading a list of guidelines intended for my girlfriend on how to deal with *me*. Like I was eavesdropping. I found a fabulous list of 'advantages' for dating an autistic man, including:

Being able to bluntly verbalise what's on their mind.

Ah, yes. What could be more romantic than bluntly verbalising what is on your mind? All the most dashing Casanovas throughout history have lain a single rose across the lap of their lover, before leaning in and whispering, 'I got one because a dozen seemed like too many even though that is also a romantic number of roses.'

Being loyal, i.e. having a slim chance of cheating on their partner.

Initially I liked this one. I would say with friends and loved ones I am loyal to a fault, as in to the extent that it has caused issues and, as a teenager, I often wondered why I seemed to take friendship to a Samwise Gamgee level and no one else did. Then I re-read it: *slim chance!?* You cheeky bastard! Nothing in there about inherent loyalty, pureness of heart, stoutness of spirit! Just a slim chance! Don't worry, love, he won't cheat – he can't! He's too astonishingly autistic to appeal to anyone else, probably, even if he wanted to!

Noticing small details about their partner that other people won't notice.

I do think this is true. Hyper-attentiveness is the product of years and years of social anxiety, missing important social cues and getting things wrong. However, it is important to note that not all small details are created equal. There is a big difference between pointing out a small detail over dinner like 'You know, your smile stays when you talk about your grandmother, but your eyes ... they become sad' and saying something like 'You have one very long eyebrow hair.'

Awareness of what their partner likes, such as a specific brand of chocolate bar, and giving them gifts of these things.

Like so much of my research into autism, this triggered a memory and realisation: I always remembered little facts like this about my first girlfriend and it was positively commented upon. I suppose if you are autistic and have loads of intense dislikes and sensory issues, you treat other people's dislikes and likes as seriously as you wish the world treated yours.

Patience, such as happily waiting for their partner to finish their drink.

Patience with situations that neurotypical people consider awkward or difficult is definitely something I can relate to. However, this means that you can misunderstand and feel like you are being patient when in reality you are missing a vital social cue. Maybe someone you are trying to date goes on a long, rambling explanation of how incredibly busy they are – what they mean is, notionally, I am too busy to date you. They might genuinely be too busy, they might be mentioning the busyness to soften the blow of them saying, 'I simply do not want to date you, I could but I don't want to.' Either way, they are putting a stop to these dating shenanigans. However, if you think that they are telling you simply in the sense of explaining an obstacle to your dating, you might think that a Nice Person would be kind and patient and wait for this awfully busy period to subside so that dating can resume. This is firmly in the category of Not Getting the Hint, but is undeniably a nice thing to do in theory. A lot of autistic people, especially women, are vulnerable to getting this patience or kindness or literalness taken advantage of. Like so much in autism, it's a double-edged sword. The finishing your drink thing is good though, I suppose.

Growing up autistic is best understood as growing up feeling wrong and being wrong. You're constantly misjudging situations and, from your point of view, getting in trouble completely out of nowhere for things that don't make any sense. Basically, your confidence in your own ability to 'get it right' in a social situation is eroded and you spend your days making a series of panicked guesses like a reluctant plane passenger figuring out, through a process of elimination, how to make an emergency landing.

Even a neurotypical person would be given anxiety by this kind of seemingly random social rejection, especially as a child, but if you couple it with an autistic sensitivity to rejection and a black and white view of the world (I am either the best partner or the worst), you end up with some difficult relationship dynamics.

Something that popped up again and again in my online research on relationship advice was that, when the non-autistic partner was upset about something to the point where they were crying, the autistic partner often wouldn't do anything. They would sit next to the crying partner but not necessarily even touch them, hold their hand or stroke their hair, often in total silence too. This was generally followed by a bunch of sad posts about how 'it seems like they don't care at all' and so on. For me, not only does that reaction make perfect sense, it's also something I have done myself. Maybe if I talk you through my thinking it will seem less crazy.

If I am with my partner and they are crying it is probably

the case that they are crying about something to do with me or us, and so I feel as though I am the guilty party. If someone was crying because you mugged them in an alleyway, or maybe bullied them at school, it would seem obscene to try to physically comfort them. It would feel like it was no longer within your rights to get to stroke their arm, say, because *you* are the cause. Additionally, there is the terror of rejection. Maybe this is formed when you're young, because when kids are crying over some silly thing and you try to soothe them they can yell out or try to fling your hand away because you are cruelly interrupting the deep, human drama of their tantrum. Your soothing hand is nothing compared to the grief of not being allowed the red cup! But it does sting to be rejected like that, and in my head if I tried to comfort a partner and then, on top of whatever problem has caused crying in the first place, we add on the emotional reaction and damage of *rejection*? I mean, forget it, our red cup runneth over with problems, and if I get upset about being rejected like that, then we are *both* upset and nothing is going to get solved.

For some autistic people it may also be that they genuinely don't understand or are finding it hard to see the reason *why* someone is crying, so there could also be the paralysis of confusion. When I was younger the stress of the situation would have rendered me almost mute, but these days I can talk to upset people. If I am not the reason for the crying, for example if a partner or friend has been bereaved, I am able to physically soothe and offer assistance of whatever kind. It would be helpful for a lot of people to know that their autistic partner isn't some awful heartless robot. In fact, it might be quite the opposite: the sheer sensitivity to their suffering is rendering them paralysed with angst. Less sympathetically, they may also not understand why you are upset and I'm afraid there will just have to be some explaining. That's obviously frustrating but hopefully it means that you aren't being deliberately obtuse or hurtful (or at least, it's not *definitely* the case. Autistic people can be assholes, too). If you're autistic, I'm afraid you may have to retrain yourself to express your feelings calmly in the moment and figure out hand-holding, hugging or whatever form of physical affection that both you and your partner can understand and accept.

Another very common problem is the frequency of compliments or positive statements. There are a lot of partners to autistic people who feel as though they have no idea what their partner thinks of them, if they find them attractive or even like them. Again, the autistic side makes more sense to me than the non-autistic side, so I'll do my best to explain.

To me, if someone says that they love me, that is true until I am told otherwise. At the very least it's true until I am given good reason to doubt it. In terms of trust, if I am going out with someone seriously enough that we have exchanged 'I love yous', then by definition I have already made the decision that this person is trustworthy. If they were someone I thought I couldn't trust, who I thought would tell me lies (nice or otherwise), then I would not date them. In fact, I'd be incapable of it! The idea of going out with someone and *still* having to spend half my energy being a Truth Detective is too exhausting and I'd resent it too much.

I once briefly dated a woman who very kindly showed me around a weird, niche museum she thought I'd like. I was very touched by the gesture but knew it was a nerdy, weird niche museum, so a few days later I made some self-deprecating comment along those lines. The woman seemed to panic and immediately assumed I'd been speaking to a mutual friend of ours: 'Oh God, have you been talking to Susan? What did she say?' and I managed to infer that this woman had been laughing with Susan about how weird and boring she found this museum trip. That killed the whole thing for me, and not just because of the feeling of being mocked for sincerely enjoying something. In my autistic mind, this meant that from now on I would have to second-guess every single nice thing this person ever did for me and figure out if it was a boring burden she would make fun of behind my back or something actually fun for both of us. Overwhelmingly stressful. It's a shame because I know there is every chance that this was purely some good-natured ribbing between her and her friend but, crucially for me, I would never be able to be certain.

The reason I describe that is to give you an idea of how *serious* it is when an autistic person decides that you are trustworthy or kind enough to be let into their life. In the mind of the autistic person, they are letting you into the inner sanctum, far beyond where any mere mortal may tread. The autistic person may presume you are in some way aware of the huge tests you have passed, and what an extremely vulnerable position they are putting themselves in by being themselves around you. Of course, you probably aren't. You probably think things are progressing in some normal way and that's entirely fair, but it's not the case.

So, given that autistic people literally mean what they say and say what they mean, if I say, 'I love you', I see no inherent need to repeat it often. If I made you repeat it over and over again, wouldn't it feel like I didn't believe you or trust you? After all, if someone *keeps* saying something, isn't it often a sign that they don't really believe it? That they're just trying to reassure themselves through repetition? And if you've grown up autistic, you are hyperaware and constantly overthinking negative signals you might give off. Never mind the fact that, if you're like me, you're completely unaware of how *often* people like to hear these things. Frankly, all of you seem deeply and insanely insecure to me. If every time I saw one of my friends they put a hand on my shoulder, stared into my eyes and calmly said 'You are my friend' then I would call the police. I think most people would.

But for partners and 'I love yous' that kind of thing at that kind of frequency is more acceptable somehow. I have done my best to say to my partner that when she gives me a lovely and intense goodbye when I go off to a gig it makes me feel like I'm heading to the Somme and unlikely to make it home. It's about making mutual adjustments, I suppose. She can say goodbye to me like I am going to die (from my perspective) and I can get her to promise that she will never touch cutlery with her teeth again. Swings and roundabouts. I have to admit I do not have a solution to the compliments frequency problem other than one of you learning to say them more and the other person accepting that insecurity is only solved from within yourself and not by external validation. I spend a lot of time telling myself that I should make sure I am being *nice* by neurotypical standards and I think I broadly manage it, but a big part of it is making sure that your partner understands that, for you, letting them rearrange your bookshelves and mix in their books is a gesture of *titanic* significance.

If you are the neurotypical partner and you fail to be flattered by these gestures, you will not survive the relationship. You need to adjust your perspective to accommodate it like you would if you were going out with an alien. If your partner tells you that, on his planet, it is a sign of only the highest love that he lets you choose where you're going to eat tonight, then you need to take it as a sign of the highest love. The adjustment has to be mutual or it's a huge, heavy neurotypical bike and only the autistic person is pedalling.

My advice to the autistic partner is to do your best to conserve some of your energy and set it aside for the task of 'noticing things about your partner' and 'giving out compliments', though unfortunately there will have to be some trial and error about what kind of compliments people like. I have certainly tried to, say, compliment someone on how confidently they did something and they have misunderstood that as some sort of veiled accusation of arrogance and shamelessness. 'I love how you don't care about what people think', for example, is a risky compliment. Keep it simple is my advice. Direct but vague positive statements about someone 'looking nice', for example. Good luck out there.

Intimacy and touch

Romantic touch generally can pose an issue if you are autistic. Some autistic people absolutely hate being touched lightly on the forearm, for example. Any light touch, especially that comes laden with social intent, is just too much – I certainly rebel a little against it. Some fellow autistic people I know hate hugs, they hate their face being lightly stroked affectionately by their lover, they hate all sorts of things that normal people love. When I say they hate it, I mean they hate it as much as a neurotypical person would hate it if someone tried to gently stroke their raw eyeball. You cringe or recoil away from it and there is no deeper form of rejection than that, so it's easy to see why it goes down so badly with neurotypical people. Especially when they cannot bring themselves to believe your explanation, any more than they'd believe you if you said you couldn't kiss them because it would summon a demon. Some autistic people have sensory issues that make physical intimacy difficult too and dealing with something as personal as that requires a huge amount of trust, patience and compassion from both partners.

The maddest thing I dislike is lying in bed with my partner face to face, if the faces are close. I hate the sensation of someone's breath so close to my mouth because I cannot get away from the idea that I am breathing in someone's breath instead of air. Even when I was a little kid, I hated this. I would go sleep in my parents' bed after a nightmare and would have to ensure that my face was pointing away from anyone else's face. Even as a kid, I knew that the air that emerged when someone breathed out was no good; it didn't have oxygen, or not enough, and so if I breathed in breath instead of air I would suffocate and die. I was totally certain of this and I never shared this belief with anyone.

I have no idea why but something common across a lot of the reflections and testimonies of autistic people is that even when they were very young kids, far before they officially had any reason to restrain themselves, they had some notion of what to keep to themselves for fear of sounding weird. I was in my thirties before I ever explained my bizarre breath terror to a partner and it takes the confidence of an adult to say, 'I know it's mad, but it's not something I can get over, so it's just going to have to be the reality we deal with.'

Rigidity in romance and fun

The preference for rigidity and predictability leads to a love of routine, and romance and routine are generally opposites for neurotypical people. Romance seems to always be about surprises, going away on holiday, changing things up. Even if your partner understands that you are autistic and understands how much you love routine, they can still think of accommodating your needs as 'doing what you want to do'. There could be some truth in this, of course, but overall it's not a fair understanding of the situation. If you gave your autistic partner a magic wand, they would probably love to wave it and turn themselves into someone who loved what you loved, who found life less difficult and stressful. The version of life they find less stressful and difficult is *not always the way they want things to be.* Certainly between the ages of sixteen and thirty I frequently wished that I enjoyed clubbing, watching football, dancing, small talk, holidays, team sport and music gigs much more than I did. It would have made life much easier socially, I would have stopped feeling such a sense of missing out on something crucial, I would have been able to feel like 'one of the young people' instead of 'technically young on paper'.

It might help you to think of your partner's need for routine as more like being lactose intolerant. It's not that they don't want to go for ice cream with you so much as they don't want to vigorously shit themselves later as a result of the ice cream. This might also help you feel more flattered, touched or grateful when they do push the autistic boat out for you – they were willing to eat all that ice cream, knowing that it would be *hell* for their arse later, *just for you.* I always felt resentful that my partners never seemed to understand or appreciate how much effort I was putting into things. It was because they never saw or understood the effort – who sees eating ice cream as hard work? Surely it's nothing but a pleasure?

Regarding the autistic love of plans, I always used to think I had managed to become a casual, chilled-out dude but I would judge that based on how uptight I had been before. If you grow from two feet tall to four feet tall, you've doubled your height, but you're not tall. Even post-diagnosis I do find it quite difficult to explain the love of, or need for, plans and expectations. If I have arranged with someone to go to a Chinese restaurant and, when I meet them, they say they'd rather go for a pizza, it's infuriating. That's the most relatable example, by the way.

To give you a less relatable one, years ago my then girlfriend told me she would come over to my flat at seven in the evening and we'd have dinner together. Great! Around five thirty, there was a knock at the door. Frowning, I opened it, expecting a misdelivered package or maybe something about a leak in the building. Standing there was my girlfriend. Because it was such a genuine surprise, and because we (in my mind) had agreed so explicitly on seven o'clock, my first reaction was worry. I knew she argued with her flatmate, for example, so maybe she was early because of that? Or some emergency?

So I said garbled something like 'Oh! You're early, what, why?' with a look of great surprise, concern and panic. She explained that she'd finished whatever it was she was doing sooner than expected and rather than have dead time she'd just come over. The trouble was, she'd seen my face and heard my tone. I am sure that my facial reaction was more 'Violent, estranged relative has surprised me by coming to Christmas lunch' than 'Aha! My beloved girlfriend! Lovely and early, what a treat!' or however you're supposed to react.

She was not happy and we had an argument about how I didn't even seem happy to see her and only seemed stressed. I tried to explain that it was only because I had mentally prepared for seven as an arrival time, but that made it seem like I saw her arrival as some traumatic event that I had to prep for, like a hurricane. My inability to easily explain my reaction to this change of plans made me seem shifty and unreliable but also made me even more stressed, because I didn't know how to explain myself. I don't know *why* it stressed me out, I would say uselessly, it just *did*. Now I was stressed about being unable to explain my stress. The whole evening could be neatly filed under 'communication failure'. Throw in some slight reluctance to be touched on the arm and you are in for an absolute *treat* of a conversation. Not that I don't get how it must have seemed – the poor woman must have thought I could barely tolerate her presence! But there was nothing I could do about it and no apparent explanation, so that was that.

There's just something about a plan that I've prepared for internally that makes me hate when it changes. I'm hungry for chow mein and now we're going for pizza? I've been thinking about chow mein all day! It's that same feeling except for a time of arrival, or the presence or lack of presence of a particular person. I feel as though my brain is a room that I have decorated and furnished in preparation for a very specific event and the change of plans is like someone breezing in and declaring that actually it's not a Halloween party, it's a baby shower, and leaving me to readjust everything on my own.

There's also the panic of no plan – as you get older, you realise how easily people allow having no plan to fuck everything up. People won't make a decision because they know everyone would be too polite to disagree with them and say what they really think. It's nice, in a way, to constantly, desperately seek reassurance that everyone is happy with every aspect of a plan, but it's exhausting and inefficient. There's also the incredibly weak phrasing people are expected to use in the United Kingdom in order to water down their own opinions and ideas and make them more palatable (and easier to contradict). You can't say, 'Let's get pizza?', you have to say, 'Well, there are a lot of options, there are some great pizza places we could go to, which I'd be happy with, but I'm happy to get Chinese or Thai if anyone is more keen on that?' Again, very considerate, but because *everyone* is trained to be like this, you end up standing on the street corner in the rain in a circle of five people listing types of food like some ritual chant. A circle of druids, intoning 'honestly, I've got no preference' until hunger pangs force one of them to volunteer to be Potentially Rude. In my opinion, if you are too shy to point out that you hate a type of food, even among friends, you deserve to frown your way through a chow mein. But that's me thinking in black and white again.

WHY CAN'T I JUST ENJOY THINGS?

Every time my partner asks me if I want to change where we are going for dinner tonight, she is being neurotypically nice by anxiously checking my opinion. It is commonly accepted as a nice, ritualistic thing to say, 'Still up for Chinese tonight?' However, in neurodivergent terms, she has just handed me a big sheet of maths homework to do. Sometimes autistic stress about plans changing isn't necessarily to do with the material change of the plans – it's stress at the sheer amount of social, non-autistic anthropology work you've just forced me to do. Right as we are about to go out, she has said, 'Hey, I am now socially forcing you to figure out which of the following statements is true':

I am double-checking you want to go to the planned restaurant because:

I am no longer in the mood for that type of food and hope you aren't either.

I am no longer in the mood to go out at all and hope you aren't either.

I am under the impression you don't like that type of food because of my non-autistic interpretation of something you said, or did, or your facial expression. You must cycle back through all of your recent behaviour and figure out why I think this because I will not tell you.

I am genuinely just checking and won't mind if you no longer want to go.

I am genuinely just checking but only out of guilt and if you don't want to go, you still sort of have to, because I'll be sad if we don't, so my question is rhetorical.

You need to work out which of these is true in order to avoid social awkwardness or, at worst, an argument. If I am exhausted and say so, but they still want to go out, then I feel like they were pretending to be considerate of my energy levels for no reason and just wanted me to lie. They also now know, even if we still go out, that I am doing something I don't want to do. No good outcome there. Calculating which of these options is the correct one (and it could be more than one! Or none! Who knows?) is so tiring that autistic people will generally learn to smile and say, 'Can't wait!' to absolutely everything that comes their way until they burn out completely. Over a lifetime this turns you into an exhausted people-pleaser, rushing around like some nervous courtier trying to stay in the favour of every lord and lady at once because the alternative is a series of exhausting calculations, followed by social gambles with incredibly stressful consequences.

If your autistic partner is a people-pleaser the imbalance of power will degrade any relationship over time. This, ironically, means that you *do* need to check in with them a lot, despite what I have literally just said about how stressful it is. However, here's the trick: they need to believe you. Just check in with them in such a way that they know you aren't being indirect or setting some social trap. Then they can answer honestly. Try not to get annoyed at an honest answer, either. I have had partners who were always furious with honest answers, despite what they said in advance, and so two things happened: I no longer believed that any of their questions were sincere and I no longer told them the truth. I don't mean I lied all the time about everything, only that I responded to their questions the way you might respond to questions from your boss at work when they ask, 'Is that clear?' or 'Happy with that?' or 'How's it going?' Treating your partner like a boss isn't exactly sustainable.

Autistic people are accused of being blunt because they correctly identify all of this social performance as a waste of energy that could be used for something else. Obviously, it's nice that Shy Mildred gets offered about a thousand chances to blurt out her actual opinion, but if we collectively agreed as a society that it wasn't rude to say what you want, we'd remove an enormous amount of the UK's collective social agony and Mildred wouldn't have to grow up shy. This will cause issues in relationships – most relationships end up with issues where two terrified people desperately try to get the other one to choose the meal or film to watch or whatever, but it's even more pronounced with autism, I find.

For example, when your partner is going to go and have dinner with a very old friend with whom they share a lot of history, they might say, 'Do you want to come?' If you are like me, your first mission is to work out if this is a neurotypical way of saying, 'You basically have to come' – the 'want' part is a kind hint or a trap instead of an actual question. In this scenario, regardless of your feelings, you have to say, 'Yes, I would love to come, there is nothing I want more on this earth' or something along those lines.

If it's not a demand disguised as a question, then the second possibility is that they are being polite or optimistically nice in a way that a lot of people are trained to be without thinking. They are saying it as instinctively as people say 'amen' after the Lord's Prayer, there's not much thought behind it. If this is the case, over the years I have managed to find polite ways to say, 'Why would I want to come and sit largely in silence while you and your friend reminisce about people I've never met and will never meet? Or discuss incredibly specific details of the very specific industry you both work in?' That experience can be unpleasant not just because the evening's conversation has no relevance to you at all, but also because it's a rudeness catch-22. Either you let them have their own optimal evening (maximum nostalgia, maximum detailed references) and sit in silence, making them feel awkward or rude, or you intervene and ask questions and get engaged in the discussion. This is polite and will remove the awkward vibe but you are reducing the potential of their optimal evening: people from decades ago will have to be explained, completely derailing whatever anecdote was taking place. Very specific details of some job or situation will have to be contextualised, destroying the momentum of the evening's conversation. You'll be like a weird little interviewer, sat there between two politicians endlessly asking them for clarification on this or that. Either way, it's a net worse outcome than if you stayed home and let the two of them get on with it.

Unfortunately, I have found that suggesting this option makes most neurotypical people incredibly anxious about you. They worry you're being left out, about whether you like them, don't like their friend, don't like where they're going to do this activity (it doesn't have to be pizza! And then we're back in the druidic circle). It will be difficult to convince your partner that, incomprehensible freak that you are, you actually *mean what you say.* If you're lucky, you'll meet someone who takes you at face value when it comes to your preferences, but it's rare and far more likely that you'll need to train them to understand you. A lot of my dislike of people asking questions they don't really mean, people revising their plans or offering to revise their plans boils down to the love of routine or familiar situations and using language literally instead of figuratively. Just remember that you are both speaking a completely different social language.

You'll also face sensory issues when doing nice romantic activities like restaurants. If you have a sensory horror of food or are a picky eater, it will probably strike the average neurotypical person as fussy at best and unromantic at worst. People respond weirdly to picky or fussy eating, either because they genuinely worry that you are having a bad time or they are irritated by what they see as childishness. The former is a benign issue that you might solve by clearly expressing that your food or sensory preferences shouldn't be taken personally. They are not a sign you are not enjoying yourself. They are simply something that you have, whether on a date or sitting at home. If they hate the fact that you are picky or have sensory issues, then you are certainly not going to be able to date them, so perhaps by showing you this early on they are saving you a great deal of time. You can spend time trying to convince them, or explain yourself without asking for their approval and see if that wins them over, but some people simply won't budge on this sort of thing. That's fine, that's their right to choose their partner, you shouldn't take it (too) personally, either.

Another issue that will come up is holidays. Some part of the neurotypical need for change, refreshing the scenery, new things or surprises means that you guys are completely obsessed with going on holiday. Culturally in the United

Kingdom it's a big thing too. It's all anyone seems to talk about; it's the safest line of small talk available after something to do with the weather and something to do with the football. 'Going anywhere nice this year?' is a question that fills me with purest dread. Family trips and stag dos aside, I didn't go on holiday for about nine years. Being a stand-up comedian involved constant travel so there was no thrill of novelty about airports and trains. Besides, if I went to visit my parents, did some weekend stag in Poland, that was enough for me for years. Comedy gigs sometimes even took me to Copenhagen, Amsterdam, Gothenburg and more. Before anyone mistakes these trips for a holiday, these visits are generally twenty-four hours long. I managed to arrive in Vienna in the early afternoon, get to my accommodation, wander around the centre for a couple of hours, do the gig, have a beer and a schnitzel and then back to the accommodation to sleep before the early-morning flight. My mind is entirely focused on the gig and I am trying to keep the gig as profitable as possible, so spending money on nice holiday things seems to defeat the point of going out there to earn money. I'm also freelance and every day I am on holiday I am losing money from work – no paid leave from my horrible boss (me). This plus going to the Fringe to work for an entire month every year meant that a holiday often seemed like insanity. I find being too hot difficult as well, from a sensory perspective.

So, whenever some well-meaning member of the British public did their *best* to socialise with me by asking me, 'Going anywhere nice this year?' I would say, 'No' like some psychopath. This would terrify them – I doubt they'd ever got this answer in their lives. Their faces would crumple for a moment as they tried to figure out if I was being rude, stand-offish, sadly admitting to being broke or maybe going on holiday but to somewhere ... shit? Of course, I could have lied, but it would have opened a can of worms:

'Going anywhere nice this year?'

Oh, God, this again. Why can't I just say 'I don't go on holiday'? Or better yet, be left alone entirely? Quick, think of something, where do people *go?* You can't say somewhere mad and expensive like Japan or Cornwall. You also sound too posh to say, like ... Blackpool. They won't believe either of those. Just say Spain. Everyone seems to constantly go on about Spain.

'Oh, uh, Spain.'

'Oh, lovely! Whereabouts?'

Fuck's sake, there's more! Where in Spain? And so on, until I break down weeping at the bus stop, too ashamed to look this old lady in the eye, crying, 'I don't know! I don't know where in Spain! I don't go on holidays!' and she kindly puts me out of my misery with one swift blow of her Zimmer frame.

There is a contradiction at the heart of a lot of this autistic self-advocacy. Even while one takes autistic concerns seriously, even while I am telling you that all I want is to be listened to and for my words to be understood as they are said, sometimes we are wrong. This is the hardest part, in my opinion: trying to guess what activity or event will be nice when it feels in advance like it's the last thing you want to do. When you are autistic, even nice things are the same as 'going to the gym'. You know you'll feel better afterwards but fucking hell, it's hard to make yourself go. My antipathy towards going on holiday did do me a lot of good in terms of saving money, focusing on work and making sure I had time to sit at home and replenish my energy levels after loads of autistic masking. However, I would have benefitted greatly from learning how to relax and let go of work, learning how to not think about work while on holiday and also getting some more fun experiences in while I was still young.

Looking back, loads of the gigs I did early on were crucial learning opportunities but some of them weren't. They were simply tedious, unfulfilling gigs that I did for the money. The trouble was that at the time they all felt utterly crucial. It might sound weird, because 'travelling the road and trying to make it as a comedian' is often the sort of thing people say they wish they had done while they were still young, but I did it when I was young and I wish I'd gone on more holidays, gone to festivals, had some adventures that didn't involve learning off by heart which regional petrol stations serve hot food after ten at night. I get the impression that if you are autistic it takes you your whole life just to figure out what you like or what will relax you, because you are learning everything longhand. Then again, I know some autistic people who have known what they liked since childhood and they simply do these same things, without any regrets or sense they are missing out on anything at all.

This attitude seems to coincide with people who were diagnosed early or not diagnosed but never masked to the extent I have. I just don't have that confidence, either because I am stuck masking or because I've done too many things I thought I'd hate and been proven wrong. I would say this complete fog of war when it comes to what is actually fun for me and what I'm doing purely to seem sociable is the hardest part of my adult diagnosis. You've got to re-figure out who you are, or at least re-confirm it. You've got to tear down the house of who you are, check all the wooden boards for rot and rebuild it again. So, heads up, fellow newbies, it'll be tough but it's worth it.

CHAPTER 15

The Future of Autism

I'm writing this in 2024 and I am excited to see how badly my idea of the future ages over the years. It could be like one of those illustrations from magazines in the early 1900s where it's captioned ENGLAND IN 1994 ACCORDING TO FUTURISTS and it's a copper-plate print of a city covered in Zeppelins, there's a kid with a steam jetpack and a woman in full, formal Edwardian petticoats just ... playing cricket?

Anyway, with the caveat that everything is constantly changing and everyone is wrong all the time, here is a non-exhaustive round-up of things that might change for autism in the future.

Terminology

It seems likely that there will be yet another change made to the DSM's or the ICD's definition of autism. The argument is already being made by some for there to be a separate 'profound autism' category or something similar, something that can adequately capture the difference between what we used to call Asperger's and ASD level 3, for example. *The Lancet*, the Autism Science Foundation and the American Centers for Disease Control and Prevention (CDC) all embrace the term 'profound autism' as a way of identifying autistic people with the highest support needs, such as autistic people with a learning disability or those who don't use speech as their primary method to communicate (though, of course, not using speech does not mean you have a learning disability). However, there is a risk that people would misunderstand 'profound autism', when used to describe someone with autism and a learning disability, to mean that an 'excess of autism' had caused the learning disability, as opposed to the two conditions being co-occurring but separate. Perhaps we could use something like 'autism WALD' (with a learning disability) to indicate the difference in support needs.

This is definitely something I would favour. It strikes me as unreasonable that I have the same label as someone who needs round-the-clock care and supervision. I think the idea that we can educate the public on the differences using ASD levels 1, 2 and 3 is to overestimate the attention span and patience of the public. I say this with great confidence as a professional 'nightclub comedian' who has greatly overestimated the patience of the public on several occasions. The message we send the public on autism has to be as simple as it can possibly be without being medically inaccurate or immoral. The average person would be able to hazard a guess at what 'care needs' might mean but it spans a huge range of possibilities. I certainly feel silly thinking of asking my live-in partner not to bite their cutlery as a 'care need' when for some people it means living in care or experiencing episodes of serious self-injury. I respect the intention of amalgamating autism under one umbrella – it's neat. It undermines the slightly eugenicist ideas some people have about functioning and intellect and what makes a person valuable *as a person*. It is scientifically more consistent than pretending Asperger's is something *completely* separate.

However, I believe there is a genuine risk that it will damage the argument for greater accommodations for the autistic population. The fusion of Asperger's and autism has led to a much wider range of people being classed as officially autistic. If you combine this with the massive increase in diagnoses from the far greater awareness we have of autism, the change in the culture of how it is viewed to have autism among the young, and long periods of forced introspection like lockdown, well, you end up with a situation where the word 'autistic' is shifting in meaning.

When I was young, someone who was autistic was someone who probably had a carer, certainly wasn't in the normal education system and would require serious help for the rest of their life. Now, I am autistic. I don't need a carer, I don't need any form of external intervention or help on a daily basis or from any state body that I can think of, and I have masked so successfully for so long that I can interpret the non-autistic world fluently with sufficient effort and energy. Any issues from autism tend to arise in private in my relationships with partners, friends, family and some adjacent health issues like hypermobility or burnout. (Then again, if anyone would like to be my personal small talk carer, that would be great. You could stand behind me, whispering meaningless things for me to say into my ear or inventing emergencies that mean I can't take part. Either would be great.)

A massive influx of people like me is causing the word autism to lose a lot of its unhealthy stigma, yes, but also a great deal of its weight and seriousness in the eyes of the non-autistic public. Just look at who they are told is autistic: activism prodigy Greta Thunberg, billionaire Elon Musk! And in fiction: eccentric science genius Sheldon Cooper from *The Big Bang Theory* and any number of God-like surgeons, detectives or computer hackers.[100] This can create unrealistic standards for autistic people, many of whom I have seen online complaining that they feel like failures for not having some autistic 'superpower'. It also misleads the public. *The Lancet* have estimated that around half of autistic people are 'profoundly autistic' or 'autistic WALD' or ASD-3, the CDC just over a quarter, but you wouldn't think it to see who represents autistic people publicly or in the public consciousness. Partly this is self-selecting bias – if you have this 'profound' autism, it is almost certain that you cannot host a seminar, publish a book or perform a show about autism in the first place, so we will likely never hear from you directly. It is irresponsible to give the public the idea that most autistic people are like these high-achieving public faces – it might lessen stigma for now, but it will be used against autistic people later.

We live in a world where, the *second* we can blame someone personally for their situation, we stop helping them.

---

100   Many of whom will be profoundly autism-coded if not explicitly autistic.

It's why we don't help homeless people until they are clean and sober, it's why we don't help criminals get rehabilitated, it's why people have such an issue with single mothers. If we convince the public that autism is *never* a disability and is actually some marvellous gift, we open up the most vulnerable autistic people to same blame-based neglect. Budgets will be cut, autism will be removed from any lists that mean employers have to take even a single step to help us, care will be denied as 'unnecessary'. If you've never dealt with overworked or unsympathetic government employees or tried to convince a bureaucracy to help you, you might think I am being overdramatic. But I am not.

I think 'autism' and 'profound autism' do a better job of clearly communicating a difference in condition to the layman than 'ASD-1, ASD-2, ASD-3', which are unhelpfully technical and sound like the names of Elon Musk's clones. However, given that 'profound autism' isn't technically accurate, it's probably better not to start adapting it – but we do need *something* that ordinary people can understand. If you question why we must make things comprehensible to the layman, I'd ask you to remember that the government is generally composed of laymen. Even in the rare cases where someone in government is very well informed on autism, they are still *elected* by laymen. The less effort the public have to put into understanding us, the more they will be willing to help us.[101]

I'm certainly not arguing for a whole new word – I think we must always use autism to describe someone with autism,

---

101 The medical establishment can continue using terms as complicated as they like, however. Go nuts! Throw some extra numbers and symbols in there, whatever you need.

regardless of what else they may live with. It destigmatises autism for people like me without separating us off from people with autism *and a learning disability.* It makes it clear that we are in the same group. The writer of *Neurotribes*, Steve Silberman, also points out how important destigmatising autism is in terms of raising the expectations of professionals and families for autistic people – you don't want to make them feel bad for not being Isaac Newton, but that's better than the other extreme where they decide you're doomed and put you in a home for your whole life and don't bother educating you. Less stigma helps adult diagnosees (like me) accept the label, and helps parents accept the label for their kids, which opens up access to special services and education.

The autistic scientist and public figure Temple Grandin theorises in her book, *Inside The Autistic Mind*, that eventually our understanding of neurology and the role of the actual physical architecture of the brain will develop to the level that we no longer even require labels such as Autism to describe such highly variable signs and symptoms. In her vision of the future, we would have an advanced enough understanding of the brain and advanced enough treatments to simply deal with things like high sensory sensitivity on a case-by-case basis, rather than feeling the need to cluster these things together. I think this might happen but that we would need firstly to completely perfect our understanding of the human brain and *then* perfect our ability to safely interact with and manipulate the very structure of the human brain. So, even if it all comes down to neural architecture, the shape of the brain, we might be talking about next-century technology, if ever.

Causality

Autism is an extremely variable and complex condition that we are only just beginning to understand. We already know that autism has several environmental and genetic factors associated with it but we still don't know *exactly* what. We know that it is very heritable, we have hundreds of genes that seem to be associated with it, but even these genes don't appear in more than a minority of autism cases. We don't even know precisely how the shape and architecture of the brain contributes to autism, much less *how* and *why* the brain becomes like that as you grow. Genes can also be affected by environment, so we will have to sift through thousands of them *and* somehow try to account for the almost infinite types of environmental factor that could interact with each gene in every possible variation and combination.

And it's not just environment adding to the pile of problems: copy number variation, epigenetics, double-hit mutations, sex-linked modifiers – the mind boggles! Genetic science has probably advanced tremendously in the time it has taken you to read this book and the introduction of machine learning will speed it up even more, so there may be a genetic breakthrough regarding autism in the next few decades. However, the factors at play are so complex there is a strong chance that we never find a simple genetic explanation.

Because autism is so variable as a condition and the people who have it are so variable (in their phenotype, e.g. genetic makeup and environment), it may be that we never reach a level of understanding or treatment that we have reached with simpler conditions. This makes autism a prime candidate for personalised medicine in the future. In the future, it may be possible to manage or even prevent co-occurring conditions of autism such as seizures using personalised medicine based on a person's specific genetic makeup. If personalised medicine sounds too futuristic for you, I'm afraid it's already here in the form of gadgets that monitor your blood sugar and insulin levels to help you perfect the exact diet that helps *you* lose weight specifically. You can even get personalised testosterone treatments that allegedly help you with things like 'being a useless little dweeb', according to the toxic and medically unsound adverts polluting my Instagram.

Alleviation

Even if there isn't a genetic explanation for autism, the research could be used to, say, alleviate some of the digestive, sleep or mood disorders than can come with autism.

The more we understand the human body the closer we get to inventing treatments that could alleviate or prevent some of autism's co-occurring conditions such as seizures or hypermobility. However, there is no medicine for autism and because it is a neurotype, i.e. a condition deeply associated with your actual brain and who you are. There will never be a pill for autism the way there is a pill for, say, erectile dysfunction and, crucially, there doesn't need to be. I am quite certain a lot of people are keen to make a lot of money from pills that claim to improve autism and I have seen some vague claims associated with both pills and gut biomes online.

That's not to say medicine can't help you at all: you can get prescribed medicine to deal with the *effects* of *being* autistic and also medicines to deal with the long list of conditions that are commonly co-occurring with autism. Conditions like ADHD, insomnia, anxiety, depression, OCD, epilepsy, joint problems or gastrointestinal problems.[102] These medicines will likely continue to improve and become more sophisticated and make being autistic easier on that basis. For now, though, every individual autistic person will just have to deal with autism on their own individual terms.

Sheer lack of data

In my obsessive research around my own diagnosis and then my research for this book, I have been struck by how often this or that thunderously significant study has involved fewer than, say, a hundred people. I know that budgets are small and subjects, especially consistent subjects, are very hard to get, but I think the future of autism lies in mass data collection. When we are dealing with something so heterogeneous, so variable, how can we be confident in the results of such small samples? We might not be happy with such small samples when researching *less* variable conditions, never mind something like autism.

Maybe once we are done using mass collection or theft of people's data to sell them sex toys and insurance scams it can be used for good. We could use it to improve our understanding of autism, the lives of autistic people, and to identify even more of the hidden signs and symptoms or associated conditions

---

102 For autistic people, chronic fatigue syndrome could be a result of chronic stress and the impact of chronic stress on the immune system – Buchan, Dr L. (2024). Voice note to author, 9 January.

of autism. We already know how necessary this is: the fact that it took autistic self-advocacy and years of internet-based accounts to get people to even take autistic burnout seriously is a failure. It's mainly a failure of principle: to simply listen to autistic people. However, it is also a failure of data availability – without the data centralising forces of the internet, even the most progressive psychologist might not have been able to pick autistic burnout out from a line-up that included non-autistic burnout and depression. The dream is: more and more studies using vast amounts of high-quality data, less reliance on studies of eleven people conducted in the last century by a suspected eugenicist.

The idea of surveying autistic people and simply asking them about what it is like to be autistic is also a bizarrely recent one – though it is partly because we have only recently taken adult autism diagnoses seriously. The double empathy problem, an enormous, important innovation in the field of autism research, was coined by Damian Milton. Dr Milton is, crucially, autistic himself. Without the involvement of autistic people in research, both as sources of data and marshallers of it, we would still be stuck in the 'autistic people are mind-blind' era of autism. We, as autistic people, would still be routinely told by scientific authorities that our feelings of empathy were either non-existent, delusional or something we misidentified. It's a horrible thought and underlines how crucial it is to make sure we do everything we can to encourage autistic self-advocacy and participation in research for the sake of both autistic people and the researchers and academics themselves.

It's called 'participatory research' and, like anything new, has already proved controversial. 'Spectrum 10K' was a 2021 genetic study of autism intended to be the largest in British history – 10,000 autistic people contributing their DNA to advance the genetic and environmental understanding of autism and its causes. However, it soon had to be paused after a backlash, partly because of some media outlets representing it as a quest for a 'cure', partly due to data sharing concerns when it came to people's DNA, partly due to concerns that research might form the basis of a prenatal test for autism. It is difficult to research preventative or curative medicine with a condition where many people who have it would not and do not want to be 'cured'. I include myself in that – it's not always easy but I try to remember that the difficulties I experience don't come from autism directly but from my environment or conditions. However, I am lucky to have fewer care needs. Then we get into the murky territory of eugenics, abortion, cures, neurotypes vs conditions, whether or not autism is a disability by itself, what it means to be who you are, the nature of the self, the morality of choice – it's a clusterfuck. It's probably a good preview of what a clusterfuck it might be if someone claimed to find a genetic cause for, say, homosexuality.

To be clear, Spectrum 10K is *very* explicit on its website that it will not look for a cure for autism, develop a prenatal test for autism and does not aim to eradicate autism. It paused the entire project for a two-year, in-depth consultation with the autistic community, the updates from which are viewable on their website. However, it's important to note that even 'participatory research' is still research where the (generally non-autistic) professionals are in total control, whereas what

Dr Linda Buchan calls 'co-production' of research involves autistic people's direct involvement and approval.[103]

It might seem to you that autistic people are getting in their own way by forcing this study to pause. If your gut reaction is irritation that a bunch of uppity autistic activists forced a potentially very valuable study to pause its work then I totally understand. However, if we look at the way the medical establishment has treated autistic people over the past 100 years, I think we can see why concerns were raised. Ultimately, it doesn't seem like such a bad thing for scientists to remember that their research involves and affects real people and that these real people must be considered, especially when they are the ones handing over their DNA.

Won't someone think of the adults?

It's only in the last few decades that autism has become seen as something that could be diagnosed in adults and women just as much as it could in male children. Even when I was trying to research my own diagnosis, before, during and after, so many of the websites and books I could find were directed at the concerned caregivers of an autistic child. The websites were festooned with patronising, slightly pathetic cartoons and full of child-specific content and advice. Earlier in this book I described similar problems when looking for relationship advice as an adult, diagnosed man – everything was from the point of view of, or advice being given to, a non-autistic woman.

---

103   Buchan, Dr L. (2024). Voice note to author, 9 January.

THE FUTURE OF AUTISM

The drastic increase in the numbers of diagnosed autistics, and especially late adult diagnoses like mine, means that the need for better research and resources for these groups is acute. Some of the adult, generally male, audience members who look into getting diagnosed after watching one of my shows cannot be expected to be helped much by a non-autistic woman's account of her divorce in the noughties and a website about how to convince your autistic child to eat vegetables. No matter what kind of autistic person you are, when it comes to research and resources the only thing we need is more, more, more.

What Would We Prefer?

I was pondering the ideal autistic society the other day. What type of society would be friendliest to autistics? When I was younger, I was obsessed with manners, or being polite versus being rude. This is partly autistic rigid thinking but also partly because me and my parents came from a society, South Africa, that was more formal and stricter than the UK. There's a lot more 'respect for your elders, go to church, hit your kids if they fuck about' down there than there's been in the UK for a long time. That's not a moral judgement in favour or against, simply an observation. What it *meant*, however, was that I always had a much clearer idea of what was socially correct. If someone was older than you, you called them uncle or aunty or sir or whatever, you said please and thank you to everything, blah blah blah. My desi friends tell me they have a similar aunty and uncle politeness system. When I was growing up, my parents were very keen to make sure my sisters and I were polite, and I always found social rules and manners reassuring. For a while, this was one of the reasons I was so envious of Victorians – those uptight weirdos had a rule for everything![104]

The Victorians had formalised ways of greeting people – you spoke to a vicar like this, a lady like this, an army officer like this, and so on. If you were a man, you shook hands standing up and never seated. You offered ladies a chair, stood if they entered the room, and so on. You dressed following a system of rules, especially on social occasions, and there was a largely consistent idea of how to behave. The Victorians even had *floriography*, the language of flowers: specific types and colours of flower for every occasion (funerals, weddings etc.), but also for feelings like disdain or secret love or I hope we become friends. Extra meaning was added by the way the flowers were held or handed over and in which hand. I can hardly think of a more comfortable way for non-verbal or socially shy autistics to convey emotionally significant messages. If you were a man and didn't show emotions much, if you loved trains, engineering projects, extremely logical decisions and didn't let emotion guide your thinking, you were the ideal. In the Victorian era, a man who expressed his emotions indirectly, through actions, didn't speak much, had an eccentric obsession and mainly wanted to sit in his study alone was a pillar of the community. Where's Father? He's in his study, cataloguing the thousands of different kinds of beetle! It must have been almost impossible to diagnose someone as autistic in a society like that.

---

104 Domestically, I mean, in their own lives for their own benefit. Obviously, internationally, they were keen on a more 'Genghis Khan' approach to Zulus, Boers, well, there's not space to list them all – let's say anyone on earth who didn't look or sound like them.

WHAT WOULD WE PREFER?

It's all the same reasons I found the army so appealing. All the stress and decision-making of what to wear, how to speak to who, all gone. You never have to ask people to do things in an insanely polite way, you give orders and receive orders. You'll never have to rewrite an email to be full of 'if it's not a problem' and 'no worries if not' and all that other disingenuous softening bullshit.

My armchair theory is that autistic people throughout history were either impossible to diagnose because their society was very rule-based (we are good at rules! We'd rarely stand out) or they ended up finding a place where their autism was perfectly suited to the environment. Imagine being autistic in the early medieval period and being given the chance to join a monastery. Rigid rules to follow, a perfect, endlessly repeatable routine every year forever, soothing repetitive chanting, social conventions, the opportunity for obsessive learning, reading and literacy, praise for eating the same bland food all the time, praise for wearing the same clothes every day, praise for spending more and more time on your own, praise for not being married or having a partner, praise for having little or no interest in normal daily life. No wonder some form of monastic life seems to have popped up throughout history in so many different societies! Again, I am not recommending we start a chain of autism monasteries, but it is an interesting example of what a more autism-friendly society *could* look like. Then again, an 'autism monastery' would surely be a huge hit in Silicon Valley if we rebranded it – I don't think it's unfair to accuse, say, Google or GCHQ of already running something of an autism monastery.

From the other end of the spectrum, autistic people

would also be fine in a society with total freedom and zero expectations. If people truly believed that the way someone else wanted to live their life was none of their business, it would remove a lot of the social problems that arise from autism because social problems are contextual and do not exist outside of context. From what I read online from other autistic people, this paradox seems common: the desire for structure *and* the ability to choose the structure. I veer between a profoundly 'retired Colonel' attitude of 'there needs to be a rule for everything' and a profoundly hippie attitude of 'just let people express themselves however they want, *maaaaan*', but I think the common factor in both visions of society is consistency. If there are going to be rules, they need to be consistent and for everyone. If there are going to be no rules, fine, I'll do what I want. Don't tell me that I can do what I want but then object when I wear headphones at work or don't bother signing a birthday card.

Another one of my armchair theories is that the appealing nature of a maximalist system of rules or freedom is why so many of the autistic people you see online are extremely committed communists, libertarians, anarchists, hardline religious believers and so on. The idea of a big system of answers and rules that covers everything using a set of texts is irresistible since it removes a major source of daily, lifelong anxiety, stress and energy expenditure. I may become a Biblical literalist, if only to free up my schedule a little.

Speaking of online, the internet is something close to an ideal autistic community. Temple Grandin has speculated on, given how prevalent autism is in science and especially computer science, how much the way a search engine works mimics autistic ways of thinking.[105] Search terms and key words are how my memory naturally works and pure logic instructions make more sense to me than emotive, intuitive instructions. Online communication is text-based, non-tonal, and a system of cartoon faces is used to express or add emotion when relevant. Sometimes people will express how they feel without words but using a short GIF or clip of a specific film or television show. Sometimes they will use endlessly repeatable meme templates that summarise complex ideas in an image instead of having to explain it using words. I can't think of many things as autistic as *that*. There's a SpongeBob meme for literally any scenario. Sadly for some, we cannot live exclusively online, so while the internet is a welcome refuge and source of valuable information and solidarity for autistic people, by itself it is not the answer to all our problems.

Ultimately the world is chaos, and we are entwined with each other whether we like it or not, so how best to proceed? Especially since 'enforcing the big book of rules that I like' has historically gone so badly. We are not the majority, so what do we do?

If autistic people are going to achieve progress then we must be pragmatic. There will always be limitations on society's ability to embrace us or our needs. These limitations are both abstract and practical. The abstract limitation is the ability of non-autistic people to empathise with, sympathise with and accept autistic people. This can always be improved but there will always be a barrier in the form of their basic inability to see things from our point of view. They can

---

105   Grandin, Temple and Panek, Richard (2013). *The Autistic Brain*, p.165.

understand that a certain texture feels agonising, for example, but they won't feel it themselves. Understanding is all we need for adjustments to be made, though. I don't really understand what it's like to have migraines but if someone gets migraines, I'm happy to accommodate them however I can.

If you are autistic, you're between 1 and 5 per cent of the population at best, not what you might call a serious voting bloc. You'll stress yourself into knots and maybe even burn out if you spend all your time on the internet or in real life desperately trying to knock some sense into people. Some of them will never, ever understand, sympathise or empathise and they *don't want to*. Do not worry: these people are a minority. Focus on getting acceptance and understanding and spreading awareness among the open-minded majority of people and you will win. We just need to reach most reasonable, thinking people and have protection under the law – we don't need everyone to agree with us, we don't need everyone to like us. We will never convince all employers, all teachers, all parents. There will always be idiots but they are in the minority and never forget their greatest weakness: they are idiots.

I see that, especially online, there are some passionate arguments for total adjustments for autistic people as opposed to, as in UK law, 'reasonable' adjustments. There is an idea that somehow total accommodation is not only achievable but that anything less is unacceptable. Now, law in the UK is mostly about the word 'reasonable' being used over and over again, because it's a flexible concept that can be used to measure whatever society believes to be fucking crackers or obvious common sense by any given judge or jury at any given time. There is a lot of potential for autistic people to be denied very basic adjustments in the workplace but also a lot of wiggle room for great gains to be made.

While it would be nice to imagine a workplace where an autistic person could gain every single accommodation they dream of, it may simply not be possible. It could even be counterproductive. Let's say that the government suddenly passes a law that requires businesses to make nothing but accommodations for all their autistic employees. That would help the autistic people who currently have jobs, but it would mean any other business that wanted to save on the costs would simply find ways not to ever hire a single autistic person again. You might think that discrimination legislation could stop that from happening – is it stopping all the other discrimination? Either way, good luck proving it if including autism on your CV means you never get interviewed. It also raises the possibility of a paradox. What if a workplace contains two or more autistic people whose accommodations are contradictory? What if one person cannot concentrate due to the perfume worn as part of a self-soothing routine by another? Do they flip a coin? Whose autism wins? This is before we get onto the issue of when an autistic accommodation could infringe on the reasonable sensory and social comfort of non-autistic colleagues. It is unreasonable to force someone to, say, make more eye contact than they are comfortable with. It might be reasonable to ask them to make sure they have showered frequently enough that their nearby colleague cannot smell body odour.

Ultimately, a workplace is a shared space and that space will have to be governed fairly to a minimum standard of fairness. Beyond that standard, it will be up to your individual judgement as to whether or not you officially invoke your rights and force change, which could be risky and make you some enemies. All we can do is ensure that, if you are autistic, you feel you are *able* to fight for fairness.

We will never be able to fully tame the chaos of the non-autistic world, so we must strive to create the chance for as much autistic comfort as possible. These are not paradoxical stances. I must accept, for example, that there will always be people who litter, but that doesn't mean I don't want there to be lots of bins available and signs that say 'No Littering' and campaigns that teach children not to litter. The population is constantly refreshing itself – people are dying and being born every day – and so any concepts like 'littering is bad', 'gay rights' or 'autism awareness' will have to be taught over and over again forever.

Unfortunately, the route to building a better society for autistic people is the long, arduous slog of raising awareness, education, legal fights and raising money. That old chestnut – boring! It would be more fun to form a rowdy mob, march towards some evil windmill and burn it down. That's not how life works. Luckily, there are loads of people smarter and more hard-working than me already out there toiling away on behalf of autistic people. Phew! So, donate to the autism charity of your choice, write to your MP and, if you can speak up when someone is misunderstanding or demonising autism, do so, and you'll be making about as big a difference as it's possible to make.[106] That being said, if someone could hurry up and

---

106   If you *can* go into medicine yourself, go viral, become an MP, address the UN, or quit your job and work for a charity, hey, go for it. Obviously that's great, but it would be ridiculous to pretend that sort of thing is easy, common or plausible for all but a few.

get everyone in Silicon Valley diagnosed and talking about it, we'd probably be a lot more influential as a group (though it would make the computer genius stereotypes even worse).

Autism and neurodivergence is having its moment. The true scale of difference is becoming clear as more and more people realise who they are, why they are the way that they are and the fact that they can live better lives. There are hundreds of thousands more of us than anyone thought. This momentum, the wave of adults and children being diagnosed, the flood of books, articles, podcasts means that we are more aware of neurodivergence now than at any previous point in history. This 'neurodivergence moment' could be our best chance at creating a better society where there is mass understanding of autism. A society where the average person not only has a better awareness of what autism is but more sympathy with it too, where being autistic or neurodivergent is not a life sentence of misery.

In this better society, it is not particularly worth remarking upon if someone has a special interest, is stimming in public or only eats certain things, much less confronting them over it. This ideal society would understand that autism is extremely variable and treat autistic people on an individual basis, both socially, professionally and medically. It's a society where workplaces don't enforce petty dress codes or rules about headphones on employees with otherwise sterling work records, and where we don't judge and value autistic people by whether or not they are geniuses, but as individuals who all have something to contribute. In this society, the education system would be able to recognise the needs of autistic people and adjust for them. I don't deny that the more dramatic adjustments would involve expensive things like specialist training, but you do not need specialist training to let an autistic child do an exam in a separate room if they find an exam hall intolerable. You just need empathy.

In this better society, the suicide rate of autistic people goes down and the employment rate of autistic people goes up. If enough employers knew about the advantages or strengths of autistic people and left their ego at the door with regards to things like wearing a tie or not wearing headphones, then autistic people wouldn't have to choose between keeping their disability off their CV and unemployment. Suicidality is higher in the autistic population and autistic people are the least-employed disabled group in the United Kingdom.

We would no longer automatically be a society where neurodivergent people are massively overrepresented in the prison population, where 15 per cent of young people in custody are not on the autistic spectrum despite only being 1 to 5 per cent of the population at most.[107] It would be a society where it is possible to get a diagnosis of autism regardless of what ethnic background you are from. A society where the medical establishment doesn't just leave autism to be a specialist area for a precious few but keeps its frontline staff, such as GPs, up to date and educated on autism.

Ideally, autism would no longer be conflated with or misunderstood as part of terrorist radicalisation and fewer autistic people would be at risk of radicalisation to begin with after progressive, understanding policies massively reduce their loneliness and isolation. In an ideal world, hundreds of

---

107   https://www.lawgazette.co.uk/features/approaching-difference/5118323.article

autistic people wouldn't be forcibly sectioned under the Mental Health Act and kept in solitary confinement as a 'temporary measure' that can see some of them locked up and away from their families for years without review, with families banned from seeing their accommodation and, in one case, the autistic person banned from brushing their teeth for five years. These are exceptional cases but the ignorance and lack of compassion towards autism they represent is not exceptional.

I am not an expert of any kind but I would be delighted if this book helps get us an inch further towards this imagined society. I hope it helps undiagnosed autistic people discover who they are, entertains the diagnosed and helps their friends, families and partners understand them better. If we are lucky, even people with no direct connection to autism will read this book and learn more about autism and in learning become more compassionate.

If you have always wondered why you can't just enjoy things, maybe now you have the answer. You don't have to be formally diagnosed to benefit from knowing. You can stop berating yourself for being overwhelmed by stress when you're just going on holiday with people you love. Maybe you'll be a little less ashamed of your hobbies when you meet new people, though I still don't like admitting I have a gaming chair. Maybe you'll accept that burnout is real and stop doing stupid things like needlessly promising yourself that you will learn the top 2,000 most-commonly-used French words – a real example of something I have been promising to do and feeling guilty for failing to do for three years. Maybe now your loved ones can understand you and you can understand them.

It feels contradictory to recommend the early diagnosis and

mass awareness that I missed out on while also claiming to be content. Why am I not more aggrieved? Because I am one of the lucky ones. I do not wish I was a different person but that doesn't mean I couldn't have been happier or healthier, earlier. When? How much did I miss out on? It's impossible to know and unhealthy to speculate. I have tried to write the book I wish I had stumbled across when I was a teenager. Maybe it will be that book for someone else. A better, easier life is possible for autistic people. It is within our grasp!

Acknowledgements

The book wouldn't have been possible without the hard work of Julien Matthews, Mary-Grace Brunker, Jack Butler and everyone else at Avalon, my editor Joe Hallsworth and everyone else at Blink, the kindness of Stuart Laws, Alex Kealy and Sara Barron who read early drafts, the patience of my partner, Jo, and the support of my family. My thanks for the hard work of my specialist reader, Dr Linda Buchan, and Dr Maria Davies for connecting us and much else. I would also like to thank Olly Smith, Emily Dean, Frank Skinner, Janine Harouni, Andrew Nolan, Fern Brady, Ben Mumford for their encouragement and advice. Also, noise-cancelling headphones.